25 Stupid Things Nurses Do To Self Destruct

Teresa Allen, RN

Joan Brady, RN

Laura Gasparis Vonfrolio, RN

Library of Congress catalog card number: 94-092408
ISBN 0-9627246-3-7

Design and Production Coordination: *Adam E. Blyn*

Printed in the United States of America

Published by
Power Publications
56 McArthur Avenue
Staten Island, New York 10312
1-800-331-6534

Dedications...

To my husband George Spinka, whose faith and encouragement saw me through this project.

TA

To my sisters, Teesh and Laura, because what we share is so very special to me.

JB

With love to my best traveling partner, Gayle Lamey. You make my working life so enjoyable!

LGV

Table Of Contents

PREFACE

There is a story, about an old farmer sitting on his porch on a warm summer evening, with his aging, ninety pound mongrel beside him. The farmer rocked quietly in his rocking chair while his dog sat beside him, howling as if he were in great pain. The dog continued to wail as the farmer smoked his pipe and ignored him. Finally, a neighbor passed by and called to the farmer, "Hey Pete, what's the matter with your dog?"

"He's sittin' on a nail," the farmer answered indifferently.

"Well, why the hell don't he get off the nail?" the neighbor asked rationally.

"Don't hurt enough, yet", the farmer answered.

It doesn't take much imagination to see the parallel between this story and what we in the nursing profession have done to ourselves. As the demands on our profession have grown and expanded, so has a feeling of discomfort and unrest. It seems we are given increasing amounts of responsibility while gradually eroding any authority we may have had. And responsibility without authority is enough to make anyone start howling.

We all know it takes a very special person to be a nurse. Not just anyone can do what we do. Unlike most highly respected professions, nursing not only requires a rigorous education, a disciplined mind, and the energy stores of an athlete, but it also requires a specific talent, a gift, that you can only be born with. No one can really teach you how to be a nurse unless you were first endowed with this "gift." Unfortunately, like many people born with great talents, we tend to take our talent for granted and to minimize its importance. Worse yet, we allow the rest of the world to forget what a great contribution we make on a daily basis to the well-being of mankind. Eventually, after enough people (including ourselves) have underestimated and underutilized our skills, talents, and significance, we become wounded.

The dog in the above story is the one who sat on the nail and he is also the only one who can get off his duff and remove the source of his pain. He can sit there howling if he wants to, and I'm sure he'll get a lot of sympathy from the occasional passer by, but that won't stop him from hurting. The only way he can hope to stop his pain, is to study the situation, recognize the source of his pain and do something about it.

Just as the first step in eliminating the dog's suffering is for him to be aware of what is causing it, so must nurses begin to understand the cause of our anguish and distress. Awareness is always the first step in the process of change. What follows is a list of twenty five things nurses do to keep ourselves sitting on that pointed, rusty nail, and it is only after we are aware of what is causing our pain that we can muster up the energy to direct ourselves away from it.

You may find yourself getting angry about some of the things pointed out in this book and rightfully so. Many of our sometimes dysfunctional coping skills are encouraged and promoted by the healthcare system itself. Many of them are more deeply embedded than that and stem from our own learned behaviors in dysfunctional families where we learned to get our needs met in degrading and inappropriate ways. That is why you may find that many of these 25 stupid things we do sometimes spill over from our professional lives into our personal lives and vice versa. So if you find yourself becoming angry at some of the observations in this book, perhaps that is a clue, a major tip off, as to what you have to work on and change.

Admittedly, change can be a scary thing, but it can also open doors to a much better way of living than what we have known in the past. Change usually signifies growth, and we need to embrace it rather than avoid it, the way that poor howling dog did.

We've been sitting on that nail for far too long. How much longer are we going to sit on it before we realize that howling isn't the answer? It's time to stop howling (everyone's ignoring us anyway), rise up off our haunches, and create an environment that no longer wounds us!

To be, or not to be-that is the question:
Whether tis nobler in the mind to suffer
The slings and arrows of outrageous fortune
Or to take arms against a sea of troubles,
And by opposing end them.

Hamlet Act III, William Shakespeare

Introduction:

A few weeks before this book was conceived, two friends of mine (fellow writers and nurses) and I were having a conversation. We were talking about a number of things. The conversation was lively and became even more so as we began sharing "war stories" about our nursing careers. You know the type of funny, heartbreaking, frustrating, and frightening stories we were sharing; stories from the trenches of hospital wards, psych units, operating rooms, emergency rooms, examination rooms, and outpatient clinics. You've been there. You know.

After an hour or so of gabbing, we were dumbstruck by the commonalty of problems and dysfunctional behavioral patterns our stories illustrated. We realized that, although we were completely different people, from vastly different backgrounds in terms of cultural mores, religious training and geographic influences, *our nursing stories were absolutely interchangeable .* We could have told each other's stories. And, because we are continuing to deal with the "side-effects" of a combined career of almost 60 years in nursing, our awareness of these problems is painfully strong and clear.

As professional writers, that realization had a powerful effect upon us. Any writer will tell you that whenever powerful human themes, patterns, and behaviors are repeated over and over, you've got your hands on a great story. And so, to make the proverbial long story short, that's how this book came to be written.

The purpose of this book is to heighten, awaken, inspire, and stimulate your awareness as a nursing professional and as a woman and human being. I add "as a woman and human being" for this reason: *In no other profession in the world is there such an overwhelming blending and blurring of the professional with the personal as there is in nursing. In our mind's eye, and in the minds of the public, our families, and our friends, we are on duty 24 hours a day, 7 days a week, 365 days a year for the rest of our lives.*

Take a minute here and think about this. Think how this influences people's impressions and perceptions of nurses. Think of the effect this has on our self-image, our self-esteem. Think how this makes us different from other people. Think about how this shapes the lives we live, the decisions we make, and the people we bring into our lives. Think about how we respond to others, and how we allow others to respond to us. What we are talking about here is how being a nurse (and women, as well, in most instances), is what drives our behavior both professionally and personally. Whether we realize it or not, it is the nurse inside us who predominately dictates our behavior. It is this psychologically *internalized nurse* who dwells in the deepest nooks and crannies of our minds and hearts who lets us continually do things that are not in our best interest. Things that stab our self-esteem. Things that suck the blood from our spirits. Things that erode and weaken our personal and professional power and influence.

It is this emotionally internalized nurse who makes us, almost compulsively at times, meet the universal needs of others while suppressing even our own most basic human needs. And as I sit here at my computer and write about this, my internalized nurse pipes up with her sanctimonious voice and says, "Yea, and that's what makes a nurse a good nurse!" "That willingness, eagerness almost, to sacrifice the self in the name of caring for others?" I ask back. And my internalized nurse replies, " Of course! What kind of nurse are you, anyhow?"

This is the *internalized culture of nursing.* And although we don't like to talk about it, and it certainly isn't talked about at any level in our education, it does exist. Oh, and by the way, you won't see anything about this in the nursing literature either! One way you can catch a glimpse of it is in what we nurses say to and about one another. For example, we praise and glorify the nurse who agrees to work two shifts because the patients "need her" due to the administration's inadequate staffing practices. We praise and stroke the nurse who comes to work with a temperature of 102 degrees and a throat that looks like chopped liver because the patients "need her" (not to mention the other nurses who are glad to see her, chopped liver throat and all).

Like it or not, this dysfunctional internal nurse helps us point the gun every time we do something stupid and metaphorically shoot ourselves in the foot. It is she who keeps us "sitting on the nail" like that pathetic dog in the preface. It is she who blocks and suppresses our anger everytime we know we should be mad enough to spit nails.

Whether we are aware of it or not, it is through a *nurse's eyes* that we see the world and ourselves within the world. This is a powerfully important concept when you think about it. And in about five seconds, your mind is going to explode with at least a zillion examples of just how true this is. While your mind is working on one of your own, I'll share a story or two.

One of my co-authors told me this story. One day she was on her way to work. She was on the street heading into the hospital complex. She was wearing her nursing uniform. At the corner, she paused to wait for traffic to clear before crossing. A well dressed woman in a Mercedes pulls up along the curb next to my friend Joan. She pushes a button and lowers the passenger side window. With breathless voice and a condescending smile she reaches across the seat and hands an envelope to Joan and says, "Excuse me, but you are a nurse, you wouldn't mind just putting this in the mailbox at the corner for me?" Joan was so shocked by this, she automatically took the envelope and watched in amazement as the woman in the Mercedes drove away.

One night after a grueling day at work where I saw a full day of complicated patients by appointment in a busy clinic, I raced home picturing a cold drink and five minutes with my feet up before worrying about dinner. Just as I stumbled inside the house, my phone began to ring. Throwing down purse, keys, the bag of groceries I picked up on the way home, I lunged for the phone before the caller could hang up. On the phone was a family member. It's always great to hear from family; however, this was a "a family crisis" call. I automatically went on red alert status as the caller filled me in on the gruesome details.

Thirty minutes later, I continued to listen as I thought about the chicken in the grocery bag that the salmonella were chowing down on, the mail waiting to be opened, the laundry that needed to be done, the two chapters I had to write that night, and a nice Glen Livet on the rocks.

By this time I was on automatic pilot. I said, "Unha." "Right." "Oh, dear" "What a jerk!" " Of course, you have a right to be upset" "Where exactly is the pain?" "Now, what antibiotic did the doctor put you on?" "Well, what color are the pills?" Finally, I got the facts, such as they were, smooth the ruffled feathers, gave a lot of "comfort tips," and sign off. As I hung up the phone, I realized not once was I asked the simple question, "Hey, how are you?"

After dinner (the chicken was only a little off), I finally settled down at my computer with a nice cold drink. The creative juices were flowing; I was about to set sail on my second wind of the evening. But, as I turned on the computer, the doorbell rang. One of my neighbors was at the door and asked if he could chat with me a minute.

His wife had developed headaches. She had been to three different doctors and two of them told her she needed to see a psychiatrist. He was outraged. He was confused. He was frustrated. His wife was refusing to take her medications. He was worried she has a brain tumor. And since I am a nurse, could I just speak with his wife sometime the next day. You know, try to figure out what might be going on with her. Forty five minutes later, my neighbor left.

He felt so much better having talked to me; he felt less worried. He just knew I could help. He told me how much better he was going to sleep that night. I told him goodnight, dead certain I wasn't going to be as lucky. Back at the computer, I realized it was 11:45 p.m. And I had to be up at 6:00 a.m. With weary resignation, I turned out the lights and staggered to bed while making a mental note to check in with my sick family member and the neighbor's crazy wife sometime the next day. Just another day in the trenches.

The simple truth is, we enjoy helping people. Nurses are excellent listeners and offer practical, no nonsense advice. We genuinely care for our family and friends. That is not the issue. The issue is, should we be expected to be the "nurse on duty" continuously. I ask you, is this such a bad thing? Well, maybe yes, maybe no. It depends. It could be a good thing if it means we are valued for our work, our intelligence, and our service. It could be a good thing if we are truly treated like professional peers and naturally included in the power and influence loop of the systems we work within. It could be a good thing if we are properly and adequately compensated for the *true value* of our work and service, rather than what administrators are willing to pay us. It could be a good thing if our professional image is strong, assertive, and progressive.

It could be a good thing if nursing educators and leaders promoted this image to the media, the public and to our government. It could be a good thing if we have the strength of will and the backbone to demand these things.

On the other hand, this *could* be a bad thing. Let's face it. This could be a very bad thing, indeed. In fact, in many instances, it is bad news for us. Let's gather our thoughts and look at the bad news scenario. Remember the premise: in no other profession in the world is there such an overwhelming blending and blurring of the professional with the personal, as there is in nursing. In our mind's eye, and in the minds of the public, our families and our friends, we are on duty 24 hours a day, 7 days a week, 365 days a year for the rest of our lives.

In this book you will read about 25 stupid things nurses do to turn this premise into a boomerang that flies back into our faces to knock the wind out of us and render us powerless.

This book was written straight from the heart. It was not an easy book to write. We hope that it will heighten your awareness and sharpen your sense of power as a nurse. As Shakespeare wrote, we must take arms against a sea of troubles, and by opposing end them.

Compassion, integrity, and honesty are three traits that nurses possess in abundance. We hope you find these traits demonstrated in the chapters to follow. Read with an open mind, and listen for the voice of your internalized nurse. Believe it. She's going to be kicking and screaming shortly.

Chapter One

We Don't Stick Together
(United We Stand; Divided We Get Replaced By Technicians.)

Nurses are intelligent people; that is a given. We can tell you how many drops per minute an IV should run in order to deliver 125 cc's in an hour. We can assess a patient from head to toe, establish priorities, and institute a plan of care within minutes. We can pick up on the subtle changes in a patient's condition long before they show up on a chemistry profile. And we are probably the only ones (including doctors themselves) who can accurately read a physician's handwriting. So why can't we read the handwriting on the wall?

What the handwriting on the wall is telling us, is that every time we fight amongst ourselves, every time we "write each other up," every time we allow one of our peers to be mistreated without standing by her and demanding corrective action, we are giving away a chunk of our power. In most cases, nurses are so busy trying to please the people whom they perceive to have power over them (supervisors, hospital administrators, and physicians, to name a few), that they willingly donate their power to the very people who will use it against them. Will it take our replacement by technicians for us to realize the strength there is in our sheer numbers?

A sad example of how much we lose by not sticking together is illustrated in the following example.

An experienced emergency room nurse was working the

night shift on the first day of that national insult we call "Nurse Recognition Week." Upon arriving at work, she was given a pair of shoelaces with little dangling red hearts and a green lollipop on which was imprinted, "You Are Our Lifesavers." This so called symbol of appreciation brought up a lot of angry feelings in the nurse, but she had to put these feelings on the back burner while she went to work.

At 11:30 p.m. a seven year old boy was brought in with multiple traumas after having been hit by a car while crossing the street with his mother. The nurse and her colleagues worked on the child's nearly lifeless body for two hours. All the while, the nurse allowed the child's mother to stand right next to her as they worked on her son. In the midst of all the chaos and performing her technical skills with the precision of a stunt pilot, this nurse also maintained her compassion. She comforted the mother as best she could as chest tubes and endotracheal tubes invaded the child's body. Finally, it became apparent that nothing more could be done to save the child and he died. The mother held her son in her arms and cried, and the nurse held the mother in her arms and cried.

Not long after that, a 52 year old man in full cardiac arrest was wheeled in. The nurse and her colleagues intubated and defibrillated him and started intravenous and central venous pressure lines. They did all they could, but it was not enough. For the second time in just a few hours, this nurse sat with a bereaved family and cried with them. Already she had been with several people during the worst events of their lives -- the loss of a child, the death of a husband and a father.

Shortly after that, this same nurse treated a nine year old girl who had to be intubated for asthma, a six month old baby having seizures, and finally, at 6 a.m., a woman who was eight-and-a-half months pregnant, bleeding massively from a placenta previa. Just as she was about to be intubated before going to the operating room, the woman squeezed the nurse's hand and told her that it had taken her eight years to get pregnant. "Is my baby going to be okay?" she asked, wide-eyed.

When the shift ended, the nurse retreated to her locker and found the green lollipop she had tossed in there at least a million years ago. Something inside her snapped at that point and she knew what she had to do. What they **all** had to do.

She gathered up five nurses from the night shift and eight from the day shift and explained that she was going to the CEO of the hospital to tell him how inadequate and downright insulting these trinkets were. She said it was important for him to understand just how much of themselves each nurse gave to every patient who came through those doors and that he should know better than to patronize them this way. Everyone agreed with her, until she asked who was coming with her. Every one of them declined, stating they were "afraid."

Feeling more disappointed in her peers than she was with the CEO, the nurse went by herself, one lone figure making a statement for her less courageous colleagues. She held the lollipop high in the air and said she understood that this, and other gifts like it, had come from him, or at least with his approval.

Then she shared with him what had taken place in one eight hour shift. She finished by telling him that she couldn't call the operating room to find out how the woman with placenta previa had made out because her heart just couldn't break one more time tonight.

The CEO began to see the light and apologized to the nurse for the condescending "gifts." The nurse accepted his apology and realized that she could forgive him because he had probably just been misinformed by the people who work for him. But she couldn't forgive were the thirteen nurses who had abandoned her and, worse yet, had abandoned themselves and their profession. And though the nurse knew she had made her point with the CEO, she would always wonder how much more of an impact they would have made if nurses would just stick together.

The fear these thirteen nurses felt in confronting the CEO of the hospital is certainly not unfounded. You wouldn't have to look very far to find a nurse who has been "punished" for speaking up. But haven't we realized yet that we are even worse off when we mutely shrug our shoulders and allow ourselves to be intimidated? Aren't we really sending out a message that it's okay to degrade us?

Change is often preceded by pain and risk. It requires an enormous amount of courage to change a system that has been historically condescending to nurses. In addition, given the urgency and intensity of our profession, it is very easy to get caught up in the day to day struggles of our jobs that sap our energy. Often we work in isolation (my patients, your patients), and we don't understand how to present a united front. We refrain from going out on a limb for ourselves, never mind for a colleague.

But, oh, what magic we could make by occasionally going out on that limb! Even if we are not quite ready to start edging out there ourselves, the very least we can do is support the ones who are already there. In the above scenario, even if none of those thirteen nurses felt they were capable of articulating precisely what they were feeling, at least one nurse was willing to try. By merely accompanying her into battle, those nurses would have made a statement that would never have been forgotten. They would have ruled in that instance!

We have all witnessed situations where nurses allowed themselves to be intimidated into subservience, and maybe we are ashamed to admit that we have participated in them. What we need are a few success stories to help us see and actually feel the goal, to help us know that it is possible to create change by sticking together.

Here is one such story.

A travel agency ran an advertisement in "The Fraternal Order of Police Journal," promoting a cruise on which some five hundred nurses were booked for one of their annual seminars. The ad depicted a voluptuous nurse with her uniform unbuttoned to reveal a rather skimpy bikini, beckoning police officers to join them on this cruise.

It didn't take long before telephones at the travel agency began ringing off the hook, and it wasn't necessarily cops calling to book themselves on the cruise. Instead, more than two hundred irate nurses called and chastised the agency for the sexist ad. Even nursing organizations and nursing journals got involved. Soon the story was being covered both on TV and in the newspapers.

Eventually, the advertising representative who was responsible for putting the ad through was suspended indefinitely. Next, the national secretary for the National Fraternal Order of Police agreed that the ad was demeaning to nurses and admitted that it "should never have run."

Speaking of sexist portrayals of nurses, do you remember a TV show called "Nightingales" in the late 1980's? It wouldn't be surprising if you don't, since the show was taken off the air in what seemed like the blink of an eye. Again, massive numbers of nurses started a letter writing campaign and bombarded not only the network and the producers of the show, but also boycotted the sponsors.

It is no accident that when we stuck together and took on the police and a major television network, we made some very valid points and were taken seriously. If we had this kind of impact on those two very powerful forces, imagine the impact we will have on the health care system when we stop bickering among ourselves and start presenting a united front!

The fact that nurses are no longer protected by federal labor law and that RNs are rapidly being replaced by registered care technicians, is one more example of how easily our power can be stolen away from us while our attention is scattered and fragmented instead of focused on a common cause: our own welfare.

It is not coincidence that " not sticking together" is the first topic we chose to discuss in this book. We feel it is the most significant as well as the most common mistake we nurses make. If we don't get this one straightened out, the remaining twenty four won't matter very much.

Chapter Two

We Are Attuned To Everyone's Needs But Our Own
(Nurse, Heal Thyself!)

If there is one group of people who can take a strength and use it so much that it becomes a weakness, it is nurses. One of our finest "gifts," the kind you can only be born with, is our uncanny ability to read people. We have an internal radar system that would make an airport control tower look like mere child's play. We immediately sense upon entering a room that our patient is anxious, lonely, or frightened. We know just what to say and how to approach him to gain his trust or soothe the loneliness.

We are tuned in to all kinds of clues that tell us what to expect from people. We can sense when a physician is frustrated, and often use our best people-pleasing skills to avert an outburst. We see a patient's relative walking toward us and know immediately that they are displeased about something. Again, we use our excellent interpersonal relationship skills to diffuse their anger.

In the emotionally charged atmosphere of the hospital, we are like giant sponges; we absorb all the spills, splashes, and explosions of other people's anger. We recognize the fear and irritability that permeate our work environment, and we go out of our way to be helpful and accommodating. We can read most people like a book and automatically know how to handle them. In these most volatile situations, we are the peace-makers.

What's interesting, however, is that we can make such astute observations about others, yet remain blind to our own needs.

Think about how many times you've done diabetic teaching with a patient. You explained the function of the pancreas and the insulin it secretes. You probably emphasized the importance of maintaining a steady glucose level, and described the strain put on the pancreas when concentrated sugars are absorbed. You stressed the importance of good nutrition. Then, when one of your colleagues asked what time you were going to lunch, you replied that you didn't have time for lunch as you grabbed a piece of chocolate from the box on the desk and washed it down with a diet soda.

Or maybe you have been working with your cardiac patient who just had a sudden bout of angina. Among other things, you may have spent some time with this patient describing the importance of stress management and perhaps taught some relaxation techniques. Then, when the admitting office called thirty minutes before the end of your shift and said they were sending you an admission, you would have cried out of sheer frustration if you'd had the time. Instead, you promised yourself you'd have a good cry after you got all your charting done, stopped at the grocery store on the way home, and made dinner. After all, you are a nurse, and you know how to postpone gratification of your needs. That is, if you even realize you have needs.

On a professional level, we know that all human beings have needs. As nurses, however, we have difficulty putting ourselves in the human being category and admitting and defining our own needs. Many of us who are astute enough to recognize those needs, feel we must stifle them and yield to the needs of others instead. This is not some inherent flaw in us, but rather a learned behavior that can be changed.

Many of us were rewarded for stuffing our feelings down as we grew up in dysfunctional environments and it shows. Have you ever noticed how many nurses seem to suffer from eating disorders? Food seems to be our drug of choice as we try to fill up feelings of emptiness and inadequacy and stuff down feelings of anger and frustration. In spite of the tremendous physical demands on our energy, one quick glance around the workplace will reveal a number of overweight and out of shape nurses.

If we didn't learn to disregard many of our feelings and needs during our formative years, we certainly learned our lesson well during the educational process in nursing. Many of us were taught throughout our nursing education to overlook abusive behavior with excuses like: "S/he can't be held responsible for lashing out at me, after all, s/he's sick," or "Dr. So-and-so really didn't mean to yell at me, he just had a really rough day in the O.R." It is truly amazing how sensitive we are to everyone's plight but our own!

Why do we decide to be a punching bag for everyone else? Just how desperate are we for other peoples' approval? Here is an all too familiar true example of that "punching bag" mentality.

A nurse was standing in the nurses' station, speaking to a physician on the phone. More accurately, the physician was doing all the talking while the nurse quietly listened and responded meekly with an intermittent "Yes, Doctor." One of the nurse's colleagues was standing next to the her. She could hear the irate tone of the physician as he shouted profanities at the nurse. When the doctor was through chastising and verbally abusing her, the nurse timidly hung up the phone.

"Did I hear Dr. So-and-so cursing at you?," her incredulous colleague asked. "Well, yes," the nurse replied. "He gets like that sometimes."

"Why did you let him talk to you that way?" asked the second nurse. "I would have hung up on him."

(Brace yourself for this all too frightening reply)

"Well, I'm pretty strong that way," the first nurse admitted humbly. "My husband talks to me like that sometimes, so I can take it"

She can *take* it?! She can *take* it?! How frightening is this? Do some of us still see the ability to "take" abuse as a sign of strength? You bet we do. You can find examples like this in almost any setting where nurses work. Why are so many of us still willing to relinquish our own basic rights to dignity and respect in order to satisfy the inappropriate needs of others to lash out at someone? Again, this is learned behavior, and the good news is, it can -- and must -- be *unlearned.*

It is easy to be horrified by this nurse's response and to criticize her. The sad truth is, more than likely, she knows no other way to handle such a situation. Even more sadly, most of us have been in her shoes at one time or another because we were never taught how to stand up to intimidating people. There are not nearly enough strong, confidant, healthy role models in nursing to go around. The result is the pitifully timid and self sacrific-ing behavior so many nurses exhibit.

If you are thinking right now that you would never have acted as meekly as the nurse in this example and that you are certain you always take care of your own needs as well as those of others, ask yourself two questions. Have you ever put off go-ing to a doctor's office when you were ill, figuring you would just have a "corridor consult" with him/her when you got to work? Have you ever done a double shift when you were almost too tired to get through the first one because the hospital *needed* you?

We are given so many opportunities in nursing to put our own needs on hold or to minimize them that it almost seems like a normal thing to do. Nurses learn to live their lives on hold. To compound the problem, the institutions in which we work en-courage this type of behavior. And why not? It serves them well.

For example, a nurse who was taking prednisone for a se-vere allergic reaction she'd had to pollen came to work one day during a hurricane. Due to the severe weather, several nursing homes in the area lost power and transported some of their venti-lator dependent patients to her floor at the hospital. Every bed on her unit was filled. Because of the urgency of the situation, the admitting office began to accept patients to be lined up along the hallways of her floor.

The nurse remembered to take her prednisone, but didn't have time to eat or go to the bathroom. She began to feel nau-seous from taking the medicine on an empty stomach, but bravely carried on, putting the needs of her patients above her own. Eventually, the nurse became exhausted and felt she was too ill to work another minute. She called her nursing supervisor, and told her that she'd been the only RN on her unit for ten hours and that she simply couldn't work like this any longer.

Foolishly, she half expected some thanks from the supervisor for sticking it out as long as she had. Not surprisingly, what she received was a reprimand for "whining" in the face of a crisis and was warned to not "even think about leaving" for several more hours.

Is it any wonder that we routinely put our needs on hold? As this example so clearly shows, even when a glimpse of healthy, normal thinking and self preservation instincts creep into our consciousness, we are immediately criticized for thinking of ourselves. The system has us right where they want us and it serves them well to keep us in this self-sacrificing mode.

But who is really keeping us stuck in this sick role? The answer is painfully simple. We are more responsible than anyone for accepting this behavior and for keeping ourselves down. In a quote from Stuart Wilde's book, **The Force,** he tells us that by *not* compromising our position, we enter into a special kind of energy:

> *This energy begins to be felt by others and, like a hippo
> potamus rising languorously from its hippopotamus
> dreams, an immense power stirs, and all sit up and taken
> notice.*

Self-help books and inspirational speakers are everywhere

and twelve step programs abound. There is absolutely no reason for anyone to stay stuck in the quagmire of self destructive behavior. Isn't this what we so passionately tell our patients?

Nurse, heal thyself!

Chapter Three

We Don't Use Our Resources

Once upon a time, there was a nurse who noticed an alarming trend among the nurses with whom she worked on the hospital unit that treated patients with tuberculosis. Nurses were coming down with T.B. in shocking numbers. In fact, over thirty nurses came down with active T.B. over a period of several months.

Now, this nurse couldn't quite figure out why no one else seemed to be alarmed about this. Even the nurses themselves seemed to be in too much shock over being diagnosed with a serious disease to show much outrage. In fact, nothing at all was said by the sick nurses, their supervisors, or the hospital administrators. It was business as usual.

When the nurse approached the unit supervisor about the problem, she was told that the only problem that existed was the poor infection control techniques used by the nurses.

This blatant cover up outraged the nurse. It just wasn't possible for over thirty nurses to become infected with T.B. secondary to "poor technique." Suspecting a much larger (and potentially more disastrous cause), the nurse did some research. Her information led her to suspect a faulty ventilation/air purification system. Fearing for the health and well-being of the entire staff and hospital patient population, she decided to take matters into her own hands. She decided to make a call. In fact, she made several anonymous calls reporting the incident.

Within a relatively short time, her initiative paid off. One day, while on the unit, the nurse saw several people walk onto the unit dressed in "space suits": the kind of suits people wear when contamination is suspected. A hospital administrator and the unit supervisor trailed the suited figures whose faces were obscured by portable respirators and hoods.

Ignoring the protests and hand wringing of the administrator and unit supervisor, the suited inspectors calmly went about their job of inspecting the unit from top to bottom. The nurse was profoundly relieved and satisfied to see the letters "OSHA" stenciled across the backs of the inspector's suits.

The results of this nurse's initiative and efforts to protect the health and safety of her co-workers and the patients of the entire hospital were impressive. The hospital was fined a hefty one million dollars. In addition, the T.B. unit was immediately shut down and patients transferred to another facility until the hospital brought the unit's infection disease control standards up to the required level.

Although this story was started with a "once upon a time," it is true. The bottom line here is that this nurse saved lives through her use of the appropriate, available resources.

This is a dramatic illustration of what we can accomplish when we use the resources available to us to bring about a change. Not all situations, of course, are this dramatic, but the message is clear. We should not overlook the multitude of resources we have available to us.

It should be understood, we are not advocating that nurses circumvent the system resources in order to make a "statement" or as a tool to ventilate our resentment or anger over issues that could be dealt with by going through the "proper channels." Indeed not.

We should go through the "chain of command" steps first. However, there are some techniques that nurses can learn to insure their efforts are taken seriously by the system.

One of these techniques involves utilizing a powerful tool that we often have in our hand or in our pocket: pen and paper. Words have great power, but the written word has the power of conviction, accountability, and legality behind it. If something is worth complaining about, or praising or changing, it is most definitely worth documenting.

We are masters at documentation. When it comes to our patient care, we document anything and everything, down to the last decimal point and smallest descriptive detail. Our documentation skills should be broadened to include other issues and other problems. A spoken complaint, question, suggestion, or recognition can so easily be ignored, misinterpreted, slandered, or distorted. Once it is spoken, it is history.

On the other hand, when a complaint, question, concern or compliment is put down in black and white on paper and entered into the "chain of command" system, it isn't so easily ignored. *Once on paper, words take on a life of their own.*

Nurses often fail to realize the power of ink and paper. Other professionals know how to put their ideas and words into written form, but how many nurses know how to write a memorandum, a proposal, or a rebuttal? How many nurses would even consider doing such a thing? How many of us even think to carry a pad and pen with us when we go to a staff meeting, or when we are called into the manager's office to discuss an issue? How many of us bother to record meeting notes or question a meeting agenda? When people see nurses showing up at meetings, conferences, or evaluations with pen and paper in hand, they will put a great deal more thought into what they say and do. Our documentation makes them accountable for their actions. The good news is that nurses are fully capable of learning to do all these things and should do them consistently and purposefully.

When something is put into writing and formally presented, a response is required. If a response does not come, send it through again until you get one. If it isn't the one you want, document the response and send a rebuttal. If at first you do not succeed, try again. Keep copies for yourself of everything you document or present. You may need them in the future.

Timely follow up is the key to any effective form of communication. Be persistent and document with the details of time, place, person, and sequence of events. Close each piece of documentation with a summary of the facts and a restatement of your original position. This may sound like a waste of time or may seem like a pointless game: However, the fact is, this is how things work in a bureaucratic system. We should make the system work *for us*, instead of against us. If that means having to "waste" some of our time by playing "games," so be it. It is both a game and a battle with high stakes, and we have the most to lose by not entering into the battle with a "take no prisoners" attitude.

There will be times when going through the proper channels will fall short of the change or response that we feel is appropriate to our given situation. When this happens our documentation records will prove invaluable in making our case elsewhere. Nurses should be aware of all their resources and legal rights, as both nurses and employees of an organization. This may mean doing some research.

Researching resources is something we can handle. We often go to great lengths to ferret our resources for our patients. We should put that same determination and skill into practice for ourselves.

Nurses should never hesitate to turn to such resources as union representation, hospital ethics hotlines or committees, suggestion boxes, hospital grievance committees, human resource departments, consumer advocacy groups, state boards of nursing, public legal aid societies, local nursing organizations or other nursing advocacy groups, or the media.

We must remember, however, that we can't expect someone to join us in fighting our battles unless we present our case accurately, objectively, and with complete documentary records. Words do hold power. Our words as nurses hold tremendous power, and when we put our words in written form and utilize the appropriate tactics and resources, our power is increased a million fold.

The time has come for nurses to wise up. The paper stream can flow two ways. There is great power in the written word. We should make sure that the "last word" is a nurse's word.

Chapter Four
We Minimize The Intangible Gift Of Nursing
(And So Does The System)

Intangible: That which cannot be touched or mentally grasped.
-The Oxford English Dictionary

When asked what she/he does for a living, have you ever seen a nurse look away and lower her head before replying in a subdued voice, "Oh, nothing much. I'm just a nurse"?

Have you ever found yourself answering this question in this manner? Have you ever found yourself moving the conversation to another subject when it's your turn to talk about your profession? If so, you aren't alone.

Why do we find ourselves, for all practical purposes, *apologizing* for being nurses? Why are we so quick to minimize what we are and what we do? Are we even aware of doing this? It's a tough question; it makes us feel uneasy. Because it can be painful, it is something we rarely allow ourselves to think about. After all, you might say, we have enough unpleasant things to think about! It is almost as if we have a *secret* to keep hidden.

So, the logical question arises, whose "secret" are we keeping? Think about this. What nurses *really do* is the best kept secret of nursing organizations, hospitals, medical associations, and hospital administrations. We are the big secret, because we are God's gift to the American health care system. Yes, you read it right. It sounds extreme when put into words and printed on a page, but it is the truth. We *are* God's gift to the American health care system.

So, why do we allow the system to minimize the intangible gift of nursing? Why do we do it to ourselves? After all, how many lawyers, doctors, or rocket scientists have you heard say, "Oh, I'm *just* a lawyer," "I'm *just* a brain surgeon," "I *just* build space shuttles." None, that's how many. Zero. It is so ridiculous, it's funny.

Conversely, how many nurses have you heard lately answer the above question by replying in a proud voice, *"I am a nurse."* Or dare to say, *"I save lives," "I relieve pain and suffering," "I make a difference in people's lives," "I comfort and heal people."* Unfortunately, the answer is almost the same.

So, do we dare say it? Do we hold our heads up and answer in a clear voice, "I am a nurse." The answer is a resounding, YES. You better believe we should say it. We are nurses. We should never apologize, minimize, devalue, hold secret, or negate the intangible gift of nursing. The following story humorously demonstrates how one nurse decided to stand up and be counted when asked the question, "What do you do for a living?" Her story says it all.

"So I went out to dinner with some doctors and their wives one night. There they were, the wives all talking about themselves. Who has a Rolex watch, whose dress came from Saks, the usual. Then they asked what it is I do for a living. I told them I'm a nurse and that I work with the one woman's husband, Harvey. The woman clutched her chest, gasped for air, and exclaimed, 'How can you handle peoples' excreta?'

"I said to myself, 'Excreta? Is that the stuff that hangs out of clams?' Obviously, I needed to educate Hannah about what it is that nurses do.

"You know, as a nurse, Hannah,' I said, 'I need to know medicine. Oh yes, I have to know all the diseases, Hannah, plus their signs and symptoms. Now you're probably wondering why, so let me tell you. Let's say your husband, Harvey, admits a patient with rule out congestive heart failure. You see, it's me, Hannah, the nurse, who is assessing that patient for shortness of breath, rales at the bases, tachypnea, tachycardia, S3, and a decreased urinary output. You see, Hannah, as a nurse, I know these are signs of congestive heart failure, so I have to call up your husband, Harvey, and tell him that his patient is in congestive heart failure.

"I also have to know, Hannah, the complications of diseases. Now, you're probably wondering why, so let me tell you. Let's say your husband, Harvey, admits a patient with an anterior wall M.I. It's me, Hannah, the nurse, who assesses this patient to be dyspneic, tachypneic, diaphoretic, and with a wedge pressure of over 25 and elevated pulmonary artery pressure. So, Hannah, I have to call your husband and tell him that his patient is having the complication of cardiogenic shock. Not only do I have to know every disease, every sign and symptom, and every complication, I also have to know pharmacology. I have to know every medication, how much to give, signs and symptoms, and side effects as well as interactions. Now, you're probably wondering why I have to know this, Hannah, so let me tell you.

"Why just the other day, your husband Harvey, ordered aminophylline. You know, Hannah, he ordered the wrong amount, enough to kill a buffalo, in fact. Now, if I had given what he ordered, the patient would have died. But no, Hannah, I called up your husband to let him know he ordered the wrong dose and he asked me, 'well what do they usually give?' I told him, Hannah, and I saved a human life.

"I also have to know the side effects of every medication I give. You see, Hannah, you have to know what you're looking for in order to find it. And I have to be familiar with interactions of medications as well. You see, when your husband, Harvey, admits a patient with a multitude of diseases, several other doctors besides Harvey are ordering medications on him. All of these medications interact with each other, Hannah. I then have to call up your husband, Harvey, and let him know about this. Besides having to know every disease, every sign and symptom, every complication, every medication, every dosage, all the interactions, you know Hannah, I also have to know dietary therapy.

"Now, you're probably wondering why I have to know dietary therapy, so let me tell you. Why, just the other day, your husband, Harvey, ordered a regular diet for someone with a Levine Shunt. You know, when someone has a Levine Shunt, a regular diet will kill him. So I had to call up your husband Harvey, and let him know this. Besides knowing every disease, every sign and symptom, every complication, every medication, every dosage, every side effect, every interaction and dietary therapy, I also have to know, Hannah, respiratory therapy.

"Now, you're probably wondering why I have to know respiratory therapy, Hannah, so let me tell you. You see, I'm the one with the patient, and when I see that patient getting short of breath, I draw an ABG, analyze it, interpret it, and then, of course, Hannah, I notify your husband. You know, Hannah, as a nurse, I have to know psychology too, because nurses deal with a multitude of people, not just Harvey, who have personality disorders. Why, just take a look at who's sitting at this table tonight.

"And so, Hannah, aren't you glad nurses know what they know? Because nurses keep patients alive and living patients pay Harvey's bills. Besides, Hannah, sooner or later we're all going to be patients, and don't you feel better just knowing how much nurses know?" As we said, this nurse's story speaks for itself!

So, exactly what is this intangible gift of nursing we are ranting and raving about here? To better define *"that which cannot be touched,"* imagine this scene in your mind's eye: *A patient in a hospital bed. IVs, catheters, telemetry, CVP lines. The patient is fearful, anxious, complaining of pain and is restless. You are on your way to check another patient and already behind with your work, but you stop in to answer the patient's call light. You automatically scan the patient and his room. You check his lines, adjust his IV flow, glance at his telemetry, and check his IV site. You glance down at his urine bag to check his output. The patient is complaining of pain, of not feeling right, of vague discomforts. You are in a hurry. Everything looks OK, but the patient still needs something. As you go through your mental*

25

check list, you speak to him in a low, calm voice. You explain what you are doing. You make positive comments about his heart rate, his color, the sound of his breathing. You touch the patient on the shoulder, the arm, the back of his hand. You open a dialogue. You give the patient permission to admit he is fearful, feels isolated, helpless. As you reposition him, place a pillow to add support to his body, straighten his sheets, you continue to talk to him. You tell him what he can expect. You tell him what is normal for his situation. You reassure him he is being monitored. You let him know someone who cares is watching over him As you work, you gradually see a shift of body language, a relaxing of tense muscles, a smoothing of facial lines, an unclenching of hands, and you suddenly know something has happened. You know he is now feeling better, calmer, in less pain. And although outwardly nothing was done to the patient, something invaluable was done for him. You practiced the art of nursing at its best.

This is the intangible gift of nursing: the ability to connect with our patients and transfer positive energy, the therapeutic use of the self to heal and nurture, and the ability to create an interpersonal bond that is conducive to healing.

This is the fine art of nursing. This is what we signed up for. This is our rich and valuable heritage. This intangible gift of nursing is what keeps us going in spite of our frustration, our exhaustion, and our frantic attempts to keep the "busy work" (the forms, the check lists, the notes) done. *This* is what makes all the other nonsense we put up with worth it. This is the essence and the art of nursing. Unfortunately, it cannot be plotted on a graph. It cannot be checked off on a worksheet. It is not listed in a Policy and Procedure Manual. It is not mentioned in a nurse's job description. It cannot be broken down into tasks, actions, or interventions. It cannot be put on a financial spreadsheet. A physician cannot write an order for it. It cannot be itemized on a patient's hospital bill. It is not reimbursable. It is not profitable.

Therefore, it is minimized, trivialized, devalued, and ignored by the powers that control how nurses practice. Most often this precious talent of nurses is simply denied. It doesn't exist. And, God help the nurse who tries to practice the *art* of nursing in this atmosphere of bottom-line, micro-managed, task oriented nursing practice. She will be punished, and that's a fact. Everyone seems to have a voice in how nurses practice, but nurses. Nurses are being forced into the position of practicing risk management versus nursing. Risk management is a sorry substitute for quality nursing and cold comfort to sick patients. We know this to be true, and so do our patients.

To illustrate this point, think about the motto you see written on police cars: "To Protect and To Serve." If this became a nursing motto, it would read like this: nurses protect the hospitals and serve the doctors. Where does that leave the patient? Where does that leave nurses? It leaves nurses focused on risk management activities more than on practicing the art of nursing.

Many administrators and managers are under the impression that risk management and nursing are synonymous. The reason for this dangerous belief is obvious. Administrators and managers don't spend much of their day at the patient's bedside. They have more important things to do. They have numbers to crunch, budgets to balance, nurse-to-patient ratios to compute, graphs to plot on computers, and meetings to attend. This is the sad place nursing management and administration has arrived.

This is what the system demands from nurse managers and nurse administrators, and if they want to keep their jobs, this is what they give the system. It is an uphill struggle for all nurses, be they staff nurses or nurse managers. However, the struggle is worth the effort.

We must never minimize the intangible gift of nursing. It is what nurses do best. It is what makes us nurses. It's what keeps us going, and it should always be celebrated and recognized. We must celebrate nursing among ourselves, and unite our voices to sing the well-earned praises of nursing. If we sing it together, our song will be heard.

Chapter Five

We Dress Like Slobs
(A Case Of Mistaken Identity)

Many of us still remember the days when nurses were required to wear a starched, pressed white uniform, complete with white hose, immaculate, white rubber soled shoes, and of course, the prim, white cap that we wore proudly as a symbol of our schools. Excessive make up and bright nail polish were discouraged, and the only acceptable jewelry besides your school pin was a wedding band and tiny stud earrings (only if you had pierced ears). For a time, even white pant suits were not allowed. If a nurse foolishly forgot to bring her cap to work, it was not at all unusual to be sent home to retrieve it. Working without a cap on your head was heresy.

Of course, this was when nursing was a lot less complicated than it is today. The tremendous advances in technology have had a definite impact on what is considered proper attire for nurses today.

Caps are rarely, if ever worn, and many schools no longer even have a cap. Nurses today work in the trenches. We bend over beds and equipment, kneel on the floor to program PCA pumps, and often jump up on beds to initiate CPR. In addition, we are frequently christened by a multitude of bodily fluids. This is no place for caps that get caught on curtains and other equipment, or for starched white dresses. We have a very physically demanding job to do and we do it best in hospital scrub suits or pants of any kind. Even our footwear has changed, from the freshly polished "Clinic" shoes to high top sneakers or running shoes.

Even though our job descriptions and expectations have changed dramatically over the years, some basic principles still apply. For instance, a clean, neat, professional appearance still inspires confidence in our patients. An ill fitting, wrinkled uniform and old, dirty tennis shoes do not.

Then, there are the nurses who dress provocatively. One has to wonder if they do this because they think sex is power; perhaps they think this is the only kind of power they have. Whatever the reason, this type of dressing on the work site only supports the erroneous and unfair portrayal of us in the media as sex kittens.

Granted, many of us were only too happy to shed the restrictions and forced conformity of years ago. We wanted to be seen as "professionals" and to be taken seriously. Many of us concluded that our mothers don't tell us what to wear anymore, so why should our employers?

But did we have to go to such extremes? Do we really think people are going to take us more seriously in a pair of old scrubs and dirty tennis shoes? Or do we feel so defeated that we just don't care what we look like anymore? We certainly dress like a group of people who are hopelessly downtrodden. Maybe that starched white uniform and perky little cap were a bit much, but one thing is for sure, it certainly set us apart from everyone else in the hospital. If you've ever been mistaken for the lab technician or the volunteer, you know what I'm talking about.

Think about the last time you boarded an airplane. You saw the flight attendant standing there, perfectly groomed and wearing a professional looking uniform that definitely set her/him apart. You may even have seen the pilot in his/her crisp, dapper uniform. There is no way you would have mistaken any one of these crew members for a fellow passenger. Tell the truth now, didn't their flawless appearance inspire confidence in you? Imagine how you would have felt if the entire crew appeared in cut off shorts, T shirts, and sandals, and were impossible to distinguish from the vacation bound passengers. There is definitely something to be said for dressing appropriately for the part you are going to play.

Case in point: A twenty nine year old man who was a heroin addict was a patient on a med/surg unit in a big teaching hospital. His nurse, who was dressed in old, white jeans with a coffee stain on them and a t-shirt with the logo of a local motorcycle shop imprinted on the back, was at the patient's bedside when he went into full cardiac arrest.

The nurse reached for the phone at the patient's bedside and called a code. Meanwhile, she called into the hallway for help and initiated one man CPR.

When the code team arrived, one of the residents pulled the nurse from the patient and told her to wait outside. The nurse tried to argue, but the resident and another member of the code team strong-armed her into the hallway. It was only after the patient had been resuscitated and was about to be transferred to the ICU that the resident came looking for the nurse ...to tell her that

31

her "boyfriend" was still alive but very unstable. It was only then that the nurse realized she had been mistaken for the crony or relative of a long-haired, unshaven heroin addict.

If you hang around in enough nursing circles today, you hear words like "empowerment," "nurse entrepreneurs," and "clinical practice." If you then look around the room at the nurses who attend seminars on these subjects (or any subject, for that matter) your first thought might be, "Gee, they're so smart and so motivated, I wonder why they dress like slobs?"

Okay, maybe too much emphasis and pressure has been put on women's looks over the years and, since nursing is a female dominated profession, this may be our way of making a statement. Fine. However, men have known the importance of "power dressing." When was the last time you saw the CEO of a company, a business person, or a stockbroker dressed like a slob? You certainly didn't see them dressed this way at work and you probably won't even find them dressed this way at home. These people understand the importance of presenting your very best self to the world, and that when you dress as though you respect yourself, others will follow suit.

Even some fashion conscious two year olds know this. Have you ever come in contact with a two year old child who has very definite opinions as to what s/he wants to wear today? They will change outfits (including socks and shoes) until they find exactly the look they want (or until you tell them they can't watch "Barney" if they change their clothes one more time). Instinctively, they know the importance of feeling good about themselves that results when they feel good about how they look. How did we forget this?

We demonstrate this lesson everyday with our patient care. When a person is sick enough to be in the hospital, their appearance is usually the last thing they think about. Hair goes uncombed, make up is forgotten, and only the barest essentials of good grooming are carried out. But take some time with that patient one day, grooming her, straightening up the room, and trading her hospital gown for her own pink pajamas, and what a difference you see! The patient actually seems to *feel physically better* when she is cleaned up, wearing make up and clothes that she feels good about. Not that good grooming will necessarily change her medical prognosis, but we've all seen a patient or two whose positive self image suddenly ignites a feeling of well-being. After that, we often see a steady stream of improvement.

After spending twelve long hours on our feet and giving little pieces of ourselves to everyone else all day, it's not surprising that nurses sometimes exhibit the same signs and symptoms that a seriously ill patient does: a lackluster appearance and a total lack of interest in anything other than mere survival.

Of all the things we can do to give our profession the shot in the arm it needs, this is the easiest to achieve as well as the most noticeable. It is interesting to note that when we show people we think enough of ourselves to take pains with our appearance, often they will be more reluctant to treat us like people who will tolerate abuse. We send out a very strong non-verbal message that we are not here to be martyrs. Think about how often you've seen a nursing supervisor dress far better than she ever did as a staff nurse. And don't forget to notice how reluctant everyone is to expect her to do anything that is seen as "beneath" her. Suddenly her appearance seems to announce that she will not be anyone's slave. Like it or not, there is an important lesson to be learned here: when we hold our heads up high and act as though we hold ourselves in very high regard, others do the same. They don't dare mistreat us.

Clearly, it is to our advantage to present ourselves as a profession that respects itself, because that respect is *highly* contagious.

Chapter Six

We Stand On Our Heads To Please People
(And It *Still* Isn't Enough)

Gone are the days when a physician walked into the nurse's station and the nurse immediately jumped up and offered her chair. Gone are the days when a physician wanted to enter a crowded elevator and a nurse would get off in order to make room for the doctor. We've certainly come a long way since those days. Or have we?

Let's start with the misnomer we call "the Nurse's Station." It is for anyone *but* the nurses. Typically, the nurse's station is filled with social workers, physical therapists, physician's, dietitians, and the unit secretary, all of whom are fighting for patient charts. Somehow, among all this chaos, nurses are expected to find the time, the space, and the chart to document accurately every event in every patient's day.

If you look through any patient's chart, you will see that the lion's share of documentation has been done by the nurse. Yet, we are frequently willing to forfeit our time and effort as we hand over the chart we just picked up to the doctor, social worker, or dietitian. Or, if we are lucky enough (or assertive enough) to hang onto the chart we're using, inevitably a patient will need us for something that cannot wait. We leave our coveted spot at the desk leaving our pen and glasses on top of the open chart to signal we will be right back. We never learn. Ultimately, when we return, someone has plopped their chart down on top of ours, moved our glasses to the side, and are now using our pen!

Rather than fight with people (mainly because it takes too much time), we sigh heavily, find a new pen, and make a mental note to get back to that chart later when everyone else is through with it. There is *always* something else we could be doing in the meantime. Maybe we could go stand on our heads in the corner of the nurse's station, just in case that would please someone too. Then again, maybe what we really need is Hollywood's solution to the problem ... canvas chairs with our names imprinted on the back so that no one will dare confiscate our rightful territory. This "squatter's rights" method just doesn't seem to work for nurses since we're usually the ones who get called away.

Like all twenty-five of the stupid things we do, however, the system contributes to a point, but we certainly add our own input too. We've all known nurses who spend their entire shift catering to the needs of everyone else while putting off the paperwork they know must be completed until the end of their shift. Instead, they wait till they feel they have "served" everyone, then sit down to do their paperwork, when they really should be home with their feet up, relaxing. These nurses never put in for the overtime hours because they know how "displeased" administration would be if they had to pay out all that overtime. Besides, these nurses secretly think they don't deserve overtime pay because they "really should have been finished by now." They don't realize that they are doing a terrible disservice to themselves and to their colleagues. By making it look like it's possible to care for an unrealistically large number of patients *and* complete all the paperwork within the time frame of their shift, they perpetuate unrealistic expectations. Maybe they should learn to do their charting while simultaneously doing a headstand. That might please someone too!

Much like good little first graders, nurses are often assigned extra little duties for each shift, like cleaning up the med room, restocking supplies, and making out tomorrow's assignment. If these chores simply *must* be done by a nurse (which seems questionable, since we have not been tested on these skills on state board examinations), one would think the nurse would at least be given time to accomplish them. Yet, we have all seen the nurse who comes in early to get her "chores" out of the way. Often, a nurse stays late because she didn't get around to the chores due to minor annoyances like doing CPR, starting IV's and assessing her patients. She may even have "wasted" a lot of her time answering the phone, since she is often asked to work without a unit clerk as well. But will she ever speak up and tell the powers-that-be that they cannot give her twelve hours worth of work and expect her to accomplish it in eight? Certainly not! This would not *please* people and then she would *really* be a failure.

The following story is a perfect example of what can be accomplished if we forget about pleasing people and turn our attention instead to informing them of the cold, hard realities.

A critical care nurse was "floated" to a med/surg unit and given an assignment that included twelve patients, eight of whom required "complete" care. As the nurse began to organize her first patient and feed her breakfast, she realized that it took at least twenty minutes to feed this patient. She realized that twenty minutes wasn't very much time to take for feeding a patient an entire meal, but it was all the time she could spare. She then calculated how long it would take to feed all twelve of her patients if she only spent twenty minutes with each of them. That would be four hours just to finish breakfast and another four hours for lunch. That would take up her entire eight hour shift right there.

This hospital had a policy that they did not pay nurses overtime unless the nurse called earlier in the shift and informed the supervisor she'd be getting out late. When the nurse called the supervisor, she was asked how she could predict getting out late since it was only eight o'clock in the morning. The nurse patiently explained her calculations, adding that if she spent a total of ten minutes doing each patient's two doses of meds, that was another two hours of her time. Furthermore, if she were able to do each patient's vital signs in five minutes, by the time she took them twice on her shift, that would add another two hours to her workload. At least ten minutes of charting on each one would add another two hours and dressing changes on the multiple decubiti that each patient had (because there wasn't enough nursing staff to turn patients frequently), would add another two hours. Add another two hours for bathing twelve people (which is only ten minutes per patient), and you have a grand total of sixteen hours worth of work to be done in eight. The saddest part, she concluded, was that this was only the "no frills" version of nursing care; just the basics without any time spent on teaching, planning, or monitoring.

"And that is how," the nurse added, "I know at eight o'clock in the morning that I'll be getting out late today."

The supervisor was dumbfounded and had no choice but to add the numbers up again. She realized that there was no way to argue with the logic of the nurse's modest calculations. Within the hour, four nurses from the emergency room were floated to the floor to help out, since it was Sunday, and Sunday mornings are notoriously slow in the E.R.

From that day on, other nurses began using the same tactic to get proper staffing. The nurse who had "started it all" by refusing to stand on her head to please others, not surprisingly, was resented by her superiors and immediately labeled a "trouble maker."

———

And then there is the matter of being asked to be a "preceptor." Most of us are so flattered that our superiors have such confidence in us, that we completely overlook the extra work and time involved. In the corporate or business world, there would surely be some kind of extra perks or perhaps a bonus to motivate us and compensate us for extending ourselves this way. In nursing, however, the fact that people will be pleased with us is motivation enough. The task itself is seen as its own reward. And if this isn't bad enough, in some cases we are the ones who are "training" the very people (technicians) who are being primed to replace us! Is there no limit to how far we will go to gain other peoples' approval?

We've all seen nurses who come to work when they are feeling ill. Pathetically, their need to please people is far stronger than their need to heal themselves (though I doubt they are pleasing anyone who becomes infected with whatever it is they have). Then there are the nurses who come in and work a shift during what is supposed to be their vacation because the unit is short-staffed. They just know how much this will please the barracudas in the staffing office who made the scheduling blunder.

And of course, Christmas and other major holidays are a virtual bonanza for the people-pleasing tendencies of nurses. You can always find at least one nurse on every unit who has sacrificed her right to spend this special day with her family, so that someone else can be off. This isn't the same thing as camaraderie or a genuine act of kindness. In this case, the nurse who has martyred herself definitely has some secondary gains in mind. She expects the approval of her co-workers, as well as the undying gratitude of the nurse who gets to spend Christmas with her family. Why don't we see that our own approval is the only kind we really need? Why is it almost every other profession seems to understand this and we still don't? Why are we so emotionally needy?

A nurse who worked in her hospital's float pool was called to the director's office. Immediately, she assumed she had done something terribly wrong on one of the floors she'd worked on recently. She supposed she was being called to the director's office to be reprimanded. Instead, she was told that the family of a teen aged boy whom she had cared for a week ago had requested that this nurse, and this nurse only, take care of their son. The boy had a craniotomy, and the director of nurses explained that he had been left unrestrained and had fallen out of his neurochair. The family was livid and was threatening to sue. They didn't trust the nursing staff anymore except for this particular nurse, whom they'd seen deliver meticulous care to their son in the past. The hospital administration felt that by having the family's "favorite nurse" care for the patient, it might soothe some ruffled feathers. Of course, the nurse was also expected to take care of four additional patients too, since five is the normal patient load on that unit.

The nurse agreed to be assigned to this patient every day she worked until he was discharged. The patient had been difficult and demanding and was considered by the nursing staff to be a handful to care for. Had the nurse been a little more savvy and a little less anxious to please, she would have realized what a wonderful position she was in to bargain both for her patient and for herself . She could easily and reasonably have insisted that she care for only this one patient since his care was so intricate and time consuming and the family was so overwrought with concern. But she didn't.

Instead, she cared for the boy everyday while running back and forth to do the best she could for her other four patients. Due to his cerebral edema, the boy sometimes lashed out at her verbally and physically, but the nurse just kept muddling through. She continued her work doing the best she could. She never thought about re-negotiating the agreement she had made. There were just too many people who would be disappointed.

Finally, she could take no more. The straw that broke the camel's back was when the boy kicked the loaded bedpan out of the nurse's hands, spattering excrement all over her and the floor. The burden of the four other patients, combined with the abusive behavior of the teen-aged boy became too much. At last, she knew it was time to admit defeat.

She descended the six flights of stairs to the director's office (she needed the time to dispel her anger), and rehearsed her concession speech all the way down. By the time she arrived at the office door and reached for the knob, she couldn't turn it. She thought about the patient, his family, and how short-staffed the unit was. Her hand slid slowly from the knob. She turned and trudged back up the six flights of stairs to finish what she had started and to keep everyone's approval, no matter what it cost her personally.

Like many of us, that nurse desperately needed to ask herself why everyone else's approval was so important to her. Why did she *automatically* please others instead of herself? That patient would certainly not have been left hanging in the lurch if the nurse had asked for the support she needed. In fact, everyone involved would probably have been far better off if that nurse could have just stopped reaching out for approval and started recognizing her own needs. Why would we rather hurt ourselves than risk losing someone's approval?

I've promised myself I'll never do that again.

Chapter Seven

We Accomplish The Impossible

A thirteen year old girl was diagnosed with a rare form of bone cancer. The only thing modern medicine could offer her was a left sided hip disarticulation. The doctors explained the procedure to the child's mother. They asked if she would prefer to talk to her daughter about it first, before any of the surgeons did. Understandably, the mother was too horrified herself to be able to discuss in a calm and reassuring manner the fact that her daughter was going to lose her leg at hip level.

Like most children, the thirteen year old girl, Amelia, was far more aware of what was going on than anyone thought. Every time the orthopedic surgeons entered her room to discuss the impending surgery, Amelia would start screaming at them to get out. She even began to throw unopened soda cans at them as soon as she heard them approaching her door. Always, the doctors would retreat, giving the child time to calm down and hoping that maybe the next time she would let them talk to her.

A nurse on the orthopedic floor overheard the doctors discussing the situation that was taking place downstairs on the pediatric unit, and asked, if perhaps, she could help. Since the child didn't know her and hopefully wouldn't associate her with the doctors who were going to take her leg off, the nurse felt certain she could establish a rapport with Amelia. Since she was a highly experienced orthopedic nurse, she felt confident that she could answer most of Amelia's questions. She felt, perhaps, she might be able to give the child a sense of confidence that everyone involved was going to help her through this nightmare.

The doctors agreed to let her try, but didn't hold out much hope that the nurse, a perfect stranger to Amelia, would get any farther past the door than they had.

The nurse asked one of her colleagues to cover for her, then went down to the pediatric unit with one of the orthopedic residents to familiarize herself with Amelia's chart. The resident waited in the nurse's station, far from any flying soda cans, and the nurse approached Amelia's room.

She tapped gently on the door frame and asked Amelia's permission to come in. The child, stunned by the fact that someone actually asked permission to enter her room, granted it. The nurse smiled warmly at Amelia and turned her attention to all the Halloween decorations she had hanging in her room. She engaged Amelia in a conversation about trick or treating and ghosts and goblins. Suddenly, Amelia began to cry softly, telling the nurse that she would probably never go trick or treating again because of her disease.

The nurse sat down on the bed next to Amelia, holding her and soothing her. The child continued crying in the comfort of the nurse's arms and began to spill out all her fears. She knew she was going to lose her leg. She hadn't needed anyone to tell her that. She told the nurse she was terribly frightened of both the surgery and the future.

With one arm still around Amelia, the nurse reached with

her other arm for a cardboard skeleton that was hanging on the end of the bed. She asked if she could show Amelia some things about the surgery so she would understand a little better what was going on.

The nurse stayed with Amelia for a long time that morning and visited with her each day thereafter, even if it meant staying after her shift to do so. To reassure and calm the young patient, the nurse used her break time to accompany the child to the O.R. If anyone had ever told the doctors that *anyone* could have had such a calming and therapeutic effect on this child, they would not have believed it. They had watched a nurse accomplish the impossible. Immediately, they thought of another patient on the sixth floor they'd like her to see as soon as she had a chance.

When the nurse returned to her unit from accompanying Amelia to the holding area in the O.R., she was informed that her patient load had been increased because one of her colleagues had gone home ill. Instead of six patients to care for, she now had nine. And she was already behind, because she'd stayed with Amelia somewhat longer than she had planned.

She paged the nursing supervisor and told her that she simply had to have more help. It would be impossible for her to give quality nursing care to this number of patients. The supervisor was not the least bit interested in hearing about the acuity levels of the nine patients. She asked the nurse why, if her patients were so heavy, she was wasting precious time on the phone complaining about it. "Do the best you can," she added, as if this would help. Accomplish the impossible is what she should have said.

Somehow, the meds were given almost on time, dressings were changed and everyone (except the nurse, of course) got fed. During the chaos of the day, one of the residents complained to the nurse that one of his patients had been reluctant to sign a consent for tomorrow's incision and drainage of an abscessed wound. The procedure had been explained over and over, but the patient wanted to think about it some more before signing the consent. The nurse said she's see what she could do.

At the end of her shift, as she stood at her locker putting her coat on, the nurse remembered the still unsigned consent. She took her coat off, went back to the patient's room and pulled up a chair. She chatted with the patient, sympathizing with the fear of amputation he expressed and reassuring him that the only procedure that would be done at this point was the incision and drainage. A little more confident now, the patient signed the consent and the nurse witnessed it. Once again, the impossible had been accomplished.

When the nurse came to work the next morning, she was greeted by a bone-weary night nurse who said that the unit had been unusually busy during the night and that two nurses from the day shift had called out sick. The nurse would be working just as shorthanded as yesterday.

Immediately, the nurse called the supervisor and said that she couldn't possibly work this short handed again. The supervisor said, "Why not? You did it yesterday." The nurse resigned herself to another chaotic day and reached for the chart rack to check the new orders. She pulled the pre-op charts first and found the same order written on all of them, "Nurse to get consent signed." At the same time, the doctors began making morning rounds. One of them called over his shoulder to her and asked if she'd had a chance yet to speak with that difficult patient on the sixth floor.

The moral of the story? There are several: Nurses who accomplish the impossible never get thanked; nurses who accomplish the impossible set themselves up for being taken for granted; nurses who accomplish the impossible are then *expected* to accomplish it again and again and again.

So what should we do, you are probably wondering by now. Does this mean that accomplishing the impossible is a big mistake? Should we just stop doing such a good job and start doing only a mediocre one?

There are two reasons why this is not a good answer. First, anyone who plans to do only a mediocre job, doesn't belong in nursing. There is no room for mediocrity when dealing with human life. Quite frankly, most nurses don't seem capable of mediocrity anyway. Second, the reward for accomplishing the impossible is the same as the reward for all of nursing. It is in the satisfaction of knowing that you made a difference in someone's life; that their burden was lightened and their pain (whether physical or psychological) was lessened because you were there. So, no, accomplishing the impossible is never a mistake.

The more accurate question is, what can we do to ensure we are *recognized and compensated* for accomplishing the impossible, rather than just being *expected* to accomplish it?

The fine art of being appreciated for anything starts with the fine art of letting people know about it in no uncertain terms. This is not the same as bragging. The difference is that when you brag, you *praise* yourself. On the other hand, when you make people aware of your accomplishments, you are simply informing them of a job well done.

In the scenario presented, the rapport the nurse established with Amelia was nothing less than a miracle. Since we document everything else we do, from giving a bed bath to clipping someone's toenails, why shouldn't we document the miracles we perform? The nurse would have been well advised to document the success of that intervention *somewhere,* even if it was on an incident report. After all, if a patient falling out of bed is considered an "incident," why shouldn't performing a miracle be an "incident" too? She should also have insisted that a copy of the documentation be put in her personnel file.

As for the request from the doctors to see a "difficult" patient for them on the sixth floor, any nurse worth her rubber soles would be only too glad to share her expertise with any patient. But realistically, we can't be running all over the hospital when we already have a set number of patients assigned to us. Perhaps the nurse should have spoken with her supervisor and made a "deal." She might have told the supervisor that she would be happy to work with this patient, however, her work load must be adjusted in such a way that would allow her time to do this. In addition, the patient could be transferred to the orthopedic unit where the nurse worked. This would make the whole process more convenient for the nurse, rather than more convenient for the internists whose service she was on. When are nurses ever going to learn to bargain?

After the nurse successfully obtained the consent for the patient with the abscessed wound, the doctors began writing orders from then on for the nurses to obtain *all* the surgical consents. The first thing the nurse should have done was to check the hospital policy to see whose responsibility it was to witness consents, since this varies from hospital to hospital. If her hospital allows nurses to witness surgical consents, which, in this case, it did, then she needed to discuss with her immediate supervisor the amount of time involved in obtaining consents. The nurse should then insist that time and work load adjustments be made to allow her time to accomplish one more of her miracles. If nurses are going to be expected to perform miracles, then the people who want those miracles are going to have to provide the time for them.

Finally, the fact that the supervisor expected the nurse to work severely understaffed, simply because she had already proved she could do it "yesterday," is one of the most challenging situations. The best thing the nurse could have done for herself was to address the situation more aggressively the first time it happened. Again, incident reports work both ways. She could have documented on an incident report a list of all the tasks she was unable to accomplish due to short staffing. Then she could have listed what her priorities were and listed everything she *did* accomplish. How can anyone be criticized for spending their time transfusing a post op patient, treating someone in congestive heart failure, and monitoring a multiple trauma victim, rather than changing a central line dressing, labeling IV tubing, and doing nursing care plans?

Until physicians and hospital administrators begin to recognize and provide the time for us to perform our miracles, we will just have to document them and learn how to bargain for them.

Chapter Eight

We Don't Trust Our Own Judgement

Nurses have excellent judgment. Our ability to assess, monitor, and deliver appropriate nursing and medical care to critically ill patients demonstrates this fact.

As nurses, we should feel confident and comfortable with our judgment. Our judgment calls have an exceedingly high rate of accuracy. We are, more often than not, right on the money when it comes to making any kind of judgment. If we weren't capable of making rational, timely assessments and judgments as nurses, we wouldn't last long at the bedside. We probably wouldn't last long anywhere within the nursing profession if we didn't have an uncanny sense of rightness about our decisions.

We should feel proud of our ability to gather limited information, process the "data," and predict what is going to happen or determine what is in the process of happening with our patients during a given time period. Nurses practice a special type of judgment that could be described as dynamic in nature. Nurses are acutely attuned to processes, to shifts within systems, to minute details, and unformed patterns of activity. Nurses have the ability to translate chaos into order and make sense of the result. We practice nursing with a special "sixth sense" that is a complicated melding of instinct, knowledge, observational skills, talent, and experience. We utilize these skills everyday with our patients.

However, the minute we walk away from the bedside, something happens. It is as if the further we walk from the bedside, the less we trust our own judgment. We have a tendency to suppress this same excellent judgment and defer to that of others.

The net result of this behavior is that we miss opportunities to promote our unique views, opinions, solutions and concerns. For example, how many times have you been in the middle of a staff meeting and observed that when the manager asks nurses for options or input, the room suddenly becomes dead silent?

Granted, there may be other reasons why nurses hesitate to speak up. Perhaps they have spoken up in the past and were ignored; or they may feel that they are simply being given lip-service when asked to express their views. These things certainly happen to nurses. Nurses are sent "double messages" all the time from managers and administrators. (This often makes us feel like we are schizophrenic, but we are the sane trying to deal with very crazy messages.) On the one hand, the manager seems to be saying, "Yes, your opinion is important," but when you offer your opinion or a solution, your idea is conveniently shelved, overlooked, or bluntly disregarded. The message here is loud and clear, "Your opinion doesn't really matter, I am just going through the motions." However, the fact remains, we shouldn't operate under a self-imposed "gag rule." Nothing will ever change if we remain silent. We must look for opportunities to highlight and demonstrate our excellent judgment.

So, we are back to the issue of judgment. Unfortunately, nurses don't usually trust their judgment beyond the patient's bedside. Because we are not routinely included in decision-making processes regarding non-patient issues, we are not comfortable with the idea of trusting our judgment in this arena. The reason for this unease isn't difficult to understand. Negative feedback has a profound effect on people's behavioral patterns. Nurses have traditionally been "pigeon-holed," relegated and restricted to monitoring, assessing, recording, and reporting activities. Otherwise, nurses are to be seen (preferably at the bedside) and not heard.

As sad as this situation is, we can turn it around to our advantage. (Turning things around isn't easy. It takes courage, guts, and dogged persistence. But, God knows, this is the stuff nurses are made of!) The first thing we must do is recognize and accept ourselves as experts within the health care industry. That's right, you read it first right here. Nurses are industry experts, and as such, we must insist that our judgment is every bit as valuable and worthwhile as anyone else's. In fact, our judgment and input is more valuable than that of many other players within the health care field.

The second thing we must do to turn things around is to believe that we are experts and behave accordingly. This also includes turning to our colleagues for support, developing professional relationships within work settings and sphere of nursing, and sticking together against the opposition. (These points are discussed at length in Chapters One and Seventeen; however, they strongly apply in this chapter also.) Believing we are experts requires an internalized broadening of our professional self image. *Changing a given belief within a very restricted, traditionalized, and sometimes punitive system is no easy task.* Nevertheless, it is what we as nurses must do in order to survive, and, more importantly, to thrive as nurses. We must support each other in developing ourselves as industry experts by supporting, rewarding, and reinforcing behaviors that demonstrate our expertise, our judgment, and our power as nurses. This will be a slow and agonizing process for many of us, but with the support of our colleagues, we can do it. Beliefs and behaviors can be changed. We must learn to trust our judgment regardless of the issue in question.

A third thing we can do to develop confidence in our judgment away from the bedside is to capitalize on the broad base of judgment confidence we already possess. In other words, if we extend and transfer confidence in our judgment from one sphere (the patient) into wider arenas (non-patient care issues), our unease and hesitancy can be more easily overcome. We must use that already existing confidence to build confidence in another area. In fact, we do this every time we learn to do something for the first time. This is precisely how we build nursing skills, and this is how we can learn to trust our judgment in all arenas. Our nursing skills, education, judgment, and wealth of experience and expertise make us imminently qualified to be involved in making decisions in areas outside the patient's bedside.

The following story is an excellent illustration of why nurses should be involved in the general decision making loop, and what can happen when we are excluded.

A hospital administrator ordered thirty new beds for the

orthopedic unit. Naturally, he did this without consulting anyone in the nursing department.

When the beds arrived, the nurses on the unit asked why they had not been consulted for their input , since there were several suggestions they would have made. Their concerns were brushed aside by administration as the new beds were brought in. The nurses dutifully accepted the beds and transferred their first patient into one.

It so happened that this particular patient was going to the O.R. that afternoon and had to be transported in the bed. The first question the nurses asked was, "Did anyone check to see if these beds will fit through the elevator doors?" They did not fit onto the elevators used for patient transport, and it was a very red-faced administrator who had to admit it.

Had anyone had the foresight or the *confidence* in the nurses' judgment to have sought their professional opinions before making a major purchase like this, the whole disaster of having to send thirty beds back to the company could have been avoided.

The fourth thing nurses must do to learn to trust their judgment is to overcome having been trained and expected to automatically defer to the judgment of others. Traditionally, nurses have been trained, disciplined, brainwashed, programmed, and bullied into deferring to the judgment of other people within the health care system. After all, who ever asks a nurse for her opinion? According to the conventional thinking of administrators, nurses aren't serious thinkers. They don't have the analytical skills necessary to make rational judgments on issues away from the bedside. They aren't encouraged or expected to form worthwhile judgments or make decisions on issues not strictly limited to nursing tasks. Within the great scheme of things, they are only nurses. Is this the image we want? Unfortunately, we have allowed this sorry state of affairs to exist for far too long. Because of the overwhelming pressure put on us by the system, we are in danger of conforming to the image they have chosen for us.

This is truly a tough issue. It is a difficult pit to heave ourselves out of, but it can be done. The following story may help illustrate what we are up against. Suspend reality for a moment and imagine there is a society that exists in which certain, selected children are trained from birth never to sing. In this society there are designated singers and non-singers. The parents of the non-singers send their children to schools with elaborate training strategies, complicated systems of rewards and punishments, and strict adherence to the rule that for a non-singing child, singing is strictly out of the question. After all, that is their job as educators of non-singing children.

The instructors are not needlessly cruel. They do allow the child to speak. The child is even allowed to listen to the singing of others. In fact, when other people sing, the kid is taught to stop whatever he is doing and listen to the singing. On very special occasions which are strictly controlled and regulated by the educators and educational system, the kid is allowed to hum a few bars.

Years pass by and the kid grows up and leaves home. Once away from home, the kid is around people who were assigned to be singers. He hears these people belting out songs in the shower, on the streets, in cars, in their office at work, and anywhere else that suits their fancy. As taught, he dutifully listens to everyone who happens to sing. However, he begins to notice that no one even turns their heads in his direction when he "hums his few bars" as allowed by the designated rules of singers and non-singers.

It's a bit frustrating for the boy, but he guesses that's just the way it is. Then he reads a book about singers and non-singers that shatters all his beliefs. This book tells him that non-singers can become singers, in spite of society's view of them. He is shocked. He is amazed. How can this be? he asks. What will happen to me if I suddenly try to be a singer? The book goes on to outline the steps he should use to transform himself from a non-singer to a singer. The book tells him that all people are born with the capacity to be singers. The book tells him that his singing voice is already inside him, he just has to learn to trust it. He would really like to be a singer, but he wonders if it is really possible. (He wonders if he can truly learn to be a singer after all these years of being a non-singer. He wonders how in the world will he ever find his singing voice after all these years.) As nurses who are trying to learn to trust their own judgment instead of automatically deferring to that of others, we are in the same situation as the non-singing boy.

Consistently and automatically deferring to the judgment and authority of others only weakens our standing as professionals. If we don't trust our own judgment enough to engage in decision making dialogues, no one else is going to trust our judgment or bother to ask for our opinion. It is as simple as that. If nurses are not perceived as having good judgment, nurses will continue to be excluded from decision making processes. The health care industry is like all other industries in that the people who make the decisions are the people with the power.

Nurses must be counted among the decision makers.

Chapter Nine

We Suppress Our Convictions

Courage mounteth with occasion.
King John, Act II
William Shakespeare

Nurses are passionate people. We feel passionately about a wide range of professional, societal, and personal issues. This is as it should be considering the nature and intensity of the work we do everyday. People place their lives in our hands and trust us to do the right thing, at the right moment, when a crisis or need arises. This is the primary responsiblity that nurses feel. Nurses take on this responsibility fully understanding what may be required of them. More importantly, nurses courageously deliver on this responsiblity every single day, risking their jobs, their mental and physical well being, and their financial security.

Well, you might ask, if the above is true, how can you say we suppress the courage of our convictions, and to what particular convictions are you referring to? How can you imply that, although nurses are courageous people, we sometimes suppress our convictions? Isn't this a contradiction?

We are courageous people and as such, we possess strong convictions. Because of this, we also frequently find ourselves faced with conflict. After all, people who don't have strong convictions rarely suffer the stress of conflict. Their behavior is rarely in conflict with their convictions because they have none.

The reason we frequently find our behavior in direct conflict with our internal convictions is simple. Ethical contradic-
tions and conflict are envitable when one works within a dysfunctional system. The first rule in any dysfunctional system is to kill
the messenger and then suppress the message. Within the health
care industry, nurses are often the bearer of bad news. It is nurses
who point out safety issues, patient care needs, shortages, ethical
violations, and a thousand other things administrators don't want
to hear. It is nurses who are penalized for speaking out and pro-
testing. We often feel that, in order to survive, we must suppress
our convictions. We find ourselves making ethical compromises
because to do otherwise would bring the wrath of a dysfunctional
system down on our heads. (See Chapter Eleven to understand
just how dysfunctional the system is that nurses face every day of
their working lives.)

Every single nurse who ever practiced has experienced this
conflict. We all have our stories. Sometimes we were the hero-
ine, and sometimes we weren't. The following story was told by a
veteran nurse and concerns an experience she had when she was
a fourth year nursing student in a training hospital while doing
her obstetrics training. (A student nurse hasn't yet been dealt the
blows the health care system can deliver. A student nurse's "courage of convictions" is fueled by her sincerity, inexperience, and
natural sense of justice. It is for this reason that new nurses find
themselves overhwelmed with conflict and behave in contradic-
tory ways.)

As a student nurse in her obstetrics rotation, she was assigned a patient in the Labor and Delivery Unit. Her patient was a 15 year old girl who had no idea what she was about to experience. She was in pain and scared to death of what was happening inside her body. The L and D rooms were full that particular day. Women (of all ages) were in their cubicles experiencing labor in various stages.

Many of the patients were teenagers. Most of them were wailing and screaming, pulling their hair, cursing, begging God to save them, throwing things, trying to get out of the bed and basically out of control. The student nurse was doing the best she could do to calm and sooth her 15 year old patient, who was having full contractions. She was also verbally combative, screaming, grabbing the student nurse's hand and uniform, vomiting, and hysterical.

It was a situation out of the student nurse's worst nightmares. Frantic to help calm the patient, she tried to coach her with the breathing exercises she had learned in her nursing class.

The noise level in the unit was just short of a major airport runway during peak flight hours. Staff nurses were running between beds trying to keep the pandemonium to a minimum and making sure nobody was delivering in their beds; medical students were everywhere poking taut, distended abdomens and plunging their gloved hands into the writhing bodies of women. She also caught a glimpse of other medical students moving between cubicles carrying clipboards and pens.

Suddenly, the student nurse was distracted by someone

standing on the other side of her patient's bed. That someone was a medical student holding a clipboard with forms attached to it and a pen. He interrupted the student nurse's attempt to calm the patient and told the student nurse to "make herself scarce." Not liking the sound of this, the student nurse surprised herself by refusing to leave the patient's side. She stonily glared at the med student and planted her feet.

The med student replied with a look and a shrug that said, "have it your own way, cutie, but keep your trap shut." He then proceeded to "talk" to the patient. He first told her how bad he felt to see her suffering. He told her nobody should have to go through what she was obviously going through. Between contractions, the patient tried to respond by grabbing hold of his white coat and begging him to stop the pains. She understood here was a "doctor" who might give her something to take away the pains. He ignored her plea for medication, but told her he had a way for her to prevent this from ever happening again. If she would just sign this form, she would never have to go through this agony again. For some bizarre reason, the nurse found herself thinking that this med student reminded her of a used car salesman.

Reaching across the patient, the student nurse grabbed hold of the clipboard to see just what the patient was supposed to sign. To the student nurse's shock, she recognized a Consent Form for a post-delivery tubal ligation. For a moment, she didn't understand what was going on. Then it hit her right between the eyes.

Without thinking about the consequences, she told the patient not to sign anything and asked the med student to step away from the patient's bed for a word. What ensued was a nasty argument about the ethics of what this med student was doing. Soon the two were shouting loud enough to be heard over the noise level. The medical student informed the nursing student that he was operating on the instructions and authority of the Chief of Staff of the Obstetrics Department and that no little nursing student was going to get in the way of doing his job. The little nursing student replied that she would see about that. The argument was so heated, people around them had paused to watch, fully expecting (and hoping to see) an exchange of blows.

Finally, word of the raging battle reached the ears of the student nurse's instructor who appeared on the scene. She immediately started questioning the student nurse about what she thought she was doing causing such a "scene" in the middle of L and D. The student nurse, on the verge of tears at this new attack on her integrity, reigned in her frustration and told the instructor what had happened. The head nurse then appeared and took charge of the medical student. The two were separated, another student was called over to take care of the patient, and the medical student and student nurse were hauled "upstairs" to face the music.

What ensued was one hell of a mess. The nursing student was threatened with dismissal from her program if she chose to pursue the issue of medical students obtaining consent for tubal ligations from young girls in the throes of labor. It was determined that the Chief of Staff of Obstetrics was, indeed, behind the whole plan. The Dean for the School of Nursing was consulted. She in turn, had meetings with the Dean of the School of

Medicine. Other meetings were held. In the meantime, the nursing student was placed on probation. The medical student was not. Several days went by and the fate of the student nurse continued to hang in the wind.

Then, one morning, the student nurse was called to the Dean of Nursing's office. There she was told that she was no longer on probation. She was no longer in any danger of being dismissed from her program. She should forget the unfortunate incident had ever happened. In fact, she was assured, the policy of obtaining consent for sterlization at the bedside of women in labor had been discontinued. The student nurse thanked the Dean for the information and went back to class. On her way back she felt ten feet tall.

The student nurse's elation wasn't just from relief at being "off the hook." The reason for the nurse's elation was the wonderful feeling of being victorious. Without telling anyone, she had written an anonymous letter to the Ethics Committee of the teaching hospital revealing the details of what medical students were doing at the bedsides of women in labor. She ended her letter stating that if the Ethics Committee failed to act, she would forward a copy of this letter to the editor of the city's main newspaper. She later graduated with honors from nursing school, and went on to spread havoc in other institutions.

This story illustrates the ethical dilemmas nurses often find themselves involved in. In addition, her solution to her dilemma demonstrated the limited options that are available to nurses within a dysfunctional system. In this story, the student nurse didn't feel she had anything to lose by acting. In fact, she was in danger of losing everything if she didn't act.

Our situations as practicing nurses who are dependent upon institutions and bureaucracies for our livelihoods is a different matter. We do have things to lose. There's no doubt about it. Standing up for our convictions can be risky business. First, we have to decide exactly what our personal and professional convictions are and what impact those convictions have on how we practice as nurses. We must also consider the impact our convictions have on our self-esteem. In other words, we must determine what will be the personal cost of *not acting* on the strength of our convictions.

It often seems that we are "damned if we do, and damned if we don't." Doing what is right often finds us "being wrong" by the hierarchy under which we work. Doing what we know is right can metaphorically place our necks on the chopping block. Tragically, we usually can't even depend on our peers and colleagues to support us when we find ourselves in the throes of an ethical dilemma. More often than not, they stand in the crowd waiting for the axe to fall.

The pressure we feel to "keep quiet," "make no waves," "let somebody else take the heat," "just turn the other cheek," and play "monkey see no evil, hear no evil, and speak no evil" is soul crushing at times.

Ethical oppression rips the heart and soul out of nurses.

Nurses bear the brunt of this ethical oppression because *nursing is the moral "conscience" of the health care system.* We take on that responsibility because we are first and foremost committed to the patient. We align ourselves ethically and morally with the patient, and we pay dearly for doing this. Nurses are the unsung heros of the health care system and the public. Nursing produces the most heroes. Consequently, we also suffer the most casualties.

As nurses, we should take time to examine, define, and reflect upon our convictions. Not only must we do this as individuals, but we must do it with our colleagues. We must take our "philosophy of nursing" out of the closet, dust it off, and hang it up for everyone to see. If we do not do this, we will flounder from indecision, squander our precious energy and, consequently, fight all the wrong battles. (Refer to Chapter Twenty One to read how we fight all the wrong battles.)

The question we must ask ourselves is: what price are we willing to pay for having the courage to stand by our convictions? It is a question that is deeply personal and complex. We do not presume to answer that question in this chapter, nor indeed, in this book. Our objective is simply to raise your awareness and to support you in that awareness. Each of us, in her or his own way, must deal with this question, and, consequently, live with the results.

Chapter Ten

We Feel Grateful To Have A Job And A Paycheck

A nurse once wrote an open letter to her hospital's administrators, in which she said, "I had great ideals when I went into nursing. I wanted to advocate for patients in the impersonal hospital setting, to help patients who were dealing with their own mortality, afraid and alone, and to find strength and support within the institution."[1]

Does this sound like a typical hospital "employee?" Hardly. This person obviously had high ideals and only the purest of intentions upon entering her first employer/employee relationship.

She goes on to say, "Well, here I am after seven years, and I find that I have become a member of this impersonal institution; to survive, I have bought and toed the party line: 'us against them'."

Now she sounds more like a typical hospital employee. It is truly amazing how quickly a hospital can pound the idealism out of even the most altruistic of us! In the nursing profession, most of us start out much like this nurse, ready to help people in any way that we can. We focus almost exclusively on our patients and helping them to get well, trusting that the institution will treat all of us fairly.

We try not to notice when our employer treats us like disobedient school children. Instead, we derive our satisfaction from knowing we are helping people. Sooner or later, however, these rewards wear thin and it becomes apparent to us that our hard earned skills are minimized and taken for granted. Furthermore, every time we go that extra mile, which we so often do in nursing, it works against us. It seems the more we do, the more we are *expected* to do, and all of our extra efforts seem to go unnoticed and unappreciated by the people who sign our paychecks. It is as though we are being punished for proving our competence.

We begin to beg for our employer's approval in the most pathetic ways: by staying late and not putting in for overtime, by completing mountains of unnecessary and redundant paperwork, and by consenting with our silence to work in dangerously under-staffed situations. Like abused little children, we make irrational excuses for our employer's blatant greed and mistreatment of us and are overly grateful for any crumb of attention they throw our way.

Once we have reached this point, there are only two choices available to us: we can crash and burn as the nurse who wrote the open letter did, or we can dip into that deep well of resourceful-ness that all nurses have and come up with a creative solution. Not that we all haven't felt what that nurse who wrote the letter was feeling, but after years of education and fine tuning our highly technical skills (to say nothing of our seemingly innate ability to "read" people), why should we be apologetic or grateful to any-one who employs us and then takes advantage of us? What we have is a perceptual problem here. We have unique talents and skills that are in high demand. Our one shortcoming seems to be that we don't recognize our own worth.

One of the most creative and also most viable solutions discussed in nursing circles today is the idea of forming corporations of nurses and marketing our skills and talents back to the institutions that used to "own" us. Only this time, it will be on *our* terms.

Now, before you start hyperventilating or throwing PVC's at the thought of giving up being exploited, consider this: the present employer/employee relationship between hospitals and nurses can generally be regarded as confrontational at best, and dysfunctional and hostile at worst. This keeps the nurse in a subservient role and renders her basically powerless in the scheme of things. However, if a hospital had to look to a corporation of nurses to staff their units, they would see us in a very different light indeed. Without us, the CEO wouldn't be driving that Mercedes or playing golf at the country club, nor would the insurance companies be reimbursing him and helping him to build new buildings while he decides to enforce a hiring freeze for nurses.

Nurses are creative people at heart, just look at all the imaginative and sometimes ingenious ideas we come up with on our nursing units on a daily basis. Have you ever used rubber gloves filled with water as a floatation device for heel decubiti? Have you ever seen someone crush a pill in the crack of the med room door when a mortar and pestle couldn't be found? Have you ever put a piece of oxygen tubing on the end of a syringe and used it for feeding a patient who couldn't chew? This caliber of creativity can't be ignored, and demands freedom of action and time to think in order to blossom to its fullest potential.

Creativity focuses on change and is only stifled by excessive supervision. Unfortunately, hospitals are notoriously resistant to change and insistent on unnecessary supervision. If we can be this creative in an environment where the bureaucracy stifles our inventiveness, imagine what we could accomplish if we had the time and the freedom to bloom!

Once we are employed in hospitals, there are definite limits set on our opportunities for professional advancement and the possibility of greater financial compensation is minimal. The scope of our practice is determined by people who know nothing about patient care and who write policies restricting the nurse's ability to fully use her knowledge and skills. Why should we let anyone do this to us or to our patients?

Another source of frustration (and control) is the lack of collegial relationships with physicians and hospital administrators. Usually, nurses are not accorded the same degree of respect for their knowledge and skill that is afforded to their colleagues in medicine and administration. If and when we are even referred to as members of the health care team (See Chapter Nineteen: We Believe We Are Part Of The Health Care Team When We're Not), we are seen as *inferior* members. We are seen more like the team's waterboys, as opposed to true "team members."

Once again, the nurse who wrote the open letter to the administrators of her hospital described our predicament well:

*On top of providing physical, emotional and spiritual care
to patients and their families, providing staff with emotional
support and supervision, dealing with the communication
gap between doctors and nurses, assisting in problem-solving
in quality assurance, organizational and documentation issues,*

adjusting to the never ending onslaught of state and federal regulatory changes, completing reams of documentation, monitoring for adequate staffing and supplies, dealing with pharmacy issues, outside referrals, doctors' orders, patient and family concerns and attending required meetings and in-service programs, how can we be expected to hold it all together without your offering help and understanding?

Does this sound like any "team" you'd want to be on? Where is the "teamwork?" Have we had enough of this yet? Why not form our own *team* and make ourselves the captains?

The formation of Nursing Corporations which then sell their skills and services back to the hospitals is a feasible and fascinating idea. Why didn't we think of it sooner?

It presents an alternative to being used and abused until we have nothing left to give. It also offers opportunities for nurses to have greater autonomy, greater financial rewards, and achievement of collegial relationships with peers and other health care professionals.

This is our ticket out of the misery hospitals have forced upon us and our patients. You can be sure they will resist this idea and try to threaten us with joblessness. But we know better. They may even try to label us as "trouble makers," "rebels," and "feminists," but there is one label that will no longer apply once we achieve complete professional autonomy: "Doormat."

As Rebecca West wrote in 1913, "I myself have never been

able to find out precisely what feminism is: I only know that people call me a feminist whenever I express sentiments that differentiate me from a doormat."

We've been doormats long enough. It has served no one but the people who bullied us into the mess they made of health care. There is a new day on the horizon for health care, and nursing only has to reach out and take what is rightfully ours.

[1] *Summers, Caryn, "The Dysfunctional Hospital Family" Revolution - The Journal of Nurse Empowerment, Summer 1993*

Chapter Eleven
We See So Much Dysfunctional Behavior, We Accept It As Normal

Mention dysfunctional behavior and every nurse will have a story. Sometimes the stories are so bizarre as to be almost humorous. Sometimes the threatened violence and intimidation are so menacing, we find ourselves upset just thinking about an incident. For instance, it isn't difficult to imagine the feelings of the nurse in this story.

In a fit of temper, a physician threw a chart across the nurse's station and hit a nurse in the back of the head, lacerating her scalp. Shocked silence befell the nurse's station. No one spoke up for fear of igniting the physician's temper even further. Without apology, the physician seated himself at the desk and calmly began writing in another chart.

Horrified to feel blood running down the back of her head, the nurse approached the physician. To her even greater horror, the physician simply looked up at her and said, "What?" She lost all composure at this point, and began threatening the doctor with filing an assault charge. Instantly, she was whisked into her unit manager's office, told to pull herself together, and find a more appropriate way to deal with a doctor who is obviously having a bad day.

When the nurse asked if she could go to the Emergency Room to be examined, her manager replied, "Don't make a big deal out of this. It's not like you lost consciousness or anything." Due to developing aphasia secondary to her head trauma, the nurse was unable to argue. Feeling both confused and disoriented, but alert enough to know she should feel guilty for over-reacting, the nurse went to back to work.

Standing in the bathroom using a compact and the mirror over the sink, she stitched up her head with a spare piece of 3.0 silk. Unfortunately, her diplopia made for sloppy needlework. As the headache progressed and her hemiparesis worsened, she took a break to drill burr holes in her head through which to suction off the spreading hematoma and relieve her cerebral edema. Once the immediate pressure was relieved, she was better able to insert her Hep Lock through which she could administer intermittent doses of Mannitol.

While preparing her meds, a sympathetic colleague inserted an indwelling foley catheter for her now neurogenic bladder. It took her much longer than usual to write her nurses notes due to the fact that she could only write a few sentences at a time before she had to vomit into the plastic garbage bag attached to her belt. However, she persevered.

She wanted to finish her shift on time because she felt it just wouldn't be fair to charge the hospital overtime just because she was disabled. A passing physician, upon noticing agonal respirations, offered to perform an emergency tracheotomy so she could at least pass her meds. Although, the physician was unable to do anything about her decorticate posturing, she was ever so grateful for her team member's compassion and help. She waited to go to the ER because she didn't feel it would be right to go on hospital time. The next day, with a heavy heart and bandaged head, she wrote a note to her ICU nurse that someone must call in sick for her since was now on a respirator and didn't think she would be able to make it in to work that day. The unit manager sent back a message that the nurse would lose all accumulated overtime for that week if she persisted in calling in sick that week. Her co-workers dropped by the ICU to tell her how bad their day was going because she had called in sick.

An administrative rep delivered a small bouquet of flowers from the hospital gift shop with a card. Upon opening the supposed get well card, the nurse found a termination slip that read, "Due to excessive use of sick time, you have been terminated from this institution. We hope you will understand we owe it to our patients to provide them with nurses who put the patient's needs first instead of their own personal concerns." Her only regret was that, due to her paralysis, she would not be able to send a thank you note for the flowers. They were lovely little daises. Thoughtfully, another small arrangement of daisies was sent to the funeral.

OK, OK, maybe we did get a little carried away here, but we certainly got your attention. You must admit, you recognize some of the potential for this type of behavior. This next story is a true one. Honest.

An operating room nurse was assisting a surgeon in a very tedious and intricate case. The nurse, intrigued by the complexity of the case, innocently asked a technical question. Without warning, the surgeon flew into a rage and, breaking sterile technique, lifted the nurse by her elbows and literally threw her against the wall, warning her *never* to interrupt him again while he was performing surgery.

The nurse hit the wall, striking her elbow on the cold tiles, and sustained a comminuted fracture of the elbow of her dominant arm. Since she never recovered full range of motion in the arm, the nurse was transferred to work on the detox unit, being unable to work in the operating room.

Upon hearing of her plight, a family friend approached the nurse with a check for several thousand dollars to obtain legal representation to sue the physician who had disabled her. The nurse declined the generous offer, stating that the whole thing was really *her* fault. After all, she *had* asked the doctor a question.

Perhaps you're still laughing at the first fictitious example of dysfunctional behavior, but is it really so different from this one? And couldn't you just cry over the *reality* of the second one?

Granted, hospitals provide a fertile field for dysfunctional behavior to occur. The unusually high-stress environment and volatile emotions found in health care settings are an expected result of the daily life and death dramas that are played out. Dysfunctional behavior can take many forms. It can be the unit secretary who has delusions of grandeur as she barks orders to the nurses. It can be the "wolf in sheep's clothing" (the CEO of the hospital), smiling benignly as he announces the hiring freeze for RN's. It can be the unit manager who uses guilt and intimidation as a management style.

Dysfunctional behavior is not always physical. In fact, much like the classic battering syndrome, it is the emotional wounds that are sometimes far more serious than the physical ones.

The problem in nursing is that we are exposed to so much of it on every level, from physicians, management, and sometimes even patients, that it is easy to forget what is normal. When we are surrounded by dysfunctional behavior, it makes it that much easier to respond in a dysfunctional manner. This, of course, only exacerbates the situation and resolves nothing.

Our two greatest weapons in battling dysfunctional behavior are awareness and self respect. Nurses must send a firm and clear message that we will neither tolerate it nor participate in it at any level.

Chapter Twelve

We Seek Out And Stay In Dysfunctional Relationships

Do you remember the story in Chapter Two (We Are Attuned To Everyone's Needs But Our Own), where a nurse listened passively on the telephone while a physician berated her and swore at her? Do you remember the part where one of her colleagues asked why she tolerated the abuse and the nurse answered that she was strong enough to take it because she was used to her husband doing the same thing to her?

Didn't you want to grab that nurse, shake her and tell her that taking abuse is *not* a sign of strength? Or perhaps you just shook your head in sad recognition of this very common behavior among nurses. You have to wonder how a group of such intelligent and highly motivated people like nurses can be so blind when it comes to the relationships they choose.

Any psychologist will tell you that we are attracted to whatever is familiar and comfortable to us in relationships, even if it is abuse that is familiar. This is a particularly sad fact for nurses since, as previously discussed, the health care system is basically a dysfunctional one. Nurses are abused to the point where many of them simply bail out of the profession because they are too tired and frustrated to fight anymore. Nurses are encouraged to be obedient, mute, and docile, and anyone who dares to defy this autocratic system is made to pay a price.

So is it any wonder that nurses seem to gravitate to the same kind of abusive relationships in their personal lives that they experience in their professional lives?

Let's go back to that *"internalized nurse"* described in the introduction of this book. She is the part of our brain that is always criticizing us for having any human weakness and praising us for putting our own needs aside and taking care of everyone but ourselves. She is the dysfunctional part of our minds that blocks and suppresses our emotions, no matter how justified and appropriate they are.

We also mentioned in the introduction, how much our professional lives as nurses influence our personal lives. We stated, "In no other profession in the world is there such an overwhelming blending and blurring of the professional with the personal, as there is in nursing. In our mind's eye and the minds of the public, our families and our friends, we are on duty 24 hours a day, 7 days a week, 365 days a year for the rest of our lives."

This blending of nursing into our personal lives sets the stage perfectly for the dysfunctional relationships we tend to seek outside of the workplace. Have you ever noticed how many nurses are involved with people who have dependencies on drugs or alcohol or who have violent and abusive behavior, or, problems with compulsive gambling?

One has to wonder if this "internalized nurse" within all of us, is quietly and persistently egging us on to become involved *only* with needy people whom we must constantly "rescue" and "fix." This seems to be our very *identity*. We see ourselves first and foremost as nurturers and problem solvers. It seems quite a natural sequence of events that we would continue to play this role in all of our relationships, not just when we're getting paid for it.

Consider what we are expected to do to our own emotions in our roles as nurses. We are expected to be non-judgmental, no matter what the circumstances, and treat each patient with dignity and respect. On the surface this may not sound like much of a task, but anyone who has taken care of an abusive patient will begin to think differently. It doesn't matter how altruistic your intentions are. However, when you are assigned to care for a patient who is under arrest for a heinous crime like murder or rape, it can be a difficult struggle to suspend judgment. When you walk into that patient's room and treat him with respect and utter professionalism, even though he may be lashing out at you, you are suppressing some very natural instincts ... and you pay a high price for doing so.

Though the above example may be an extreme one, we experience the need to suppress our own very appropriate emotions on a daily basis. After a while, we become quite adept at stuffing down our feelings. Eventually, we don't even recognize that we have them. We make excuses for the irate surgeon who throws a temper tantrum in the nurse's station; we offer to help an overburdened colleague, even though we are far behind in our own duties; we pull up a chair and listen sympathetically to a patient, while our own lives may be falling apart at the seams. We learn to ignore what *we* are feeling and actually become quite good at hiding it, both from ourselves and from our colleagues. We do this because, usually, given the high stress environment in which we work, it is the only way we can function.

It is no surprise that we bring this dysfunctional behavior home with us. How could we possibly stuff our feelings down for eight hours, then come home and be authentic with ourselves? We have so much *stuff* to get out at the end of the day that it might take the rest of the day to resolve it all. So we go along, stuffing down *all* of our feelings and needs, making ourselves prime targets for people who will take advantage of us.

Sometimes we ask if there is a sign on our foreheads that says "SUCKER," because needy and dysfunctional people seem to be able to pick us out of a crowd. But often, if we look very closely at ourselves, we must admit that we also get satisfaction from being the one to rescue others, direct them or hold it all together while they are making a mess of their lives and ours. After all, this is what we do best, and we pride ourselves on being able to handle it.

Many of us are "crisis junkies." We are faced with life and death crises every day in our jobs and are expected to rise to the occasion. These crises often make us feel "alive" and indispensable. After a while, a relationship devoid of chronic crises can seem boring.

At work, we accomplish the impossible, yet recognition and rewards are few. We learn to keep our expectations very low, then wonder why we find ourselves in relationships that are far beneath what we deserve.

The obvious pattern here is that all of these typical behaviors in nursing - verbal and sometimes physical abuse, suppressing our emotions, catering to needy people, managing constant crises and keeping our expectations low - begin to feel comfortable and familiar. Hence, we find ourselves drawn and attracted to the same patterns in our personal lives.

The outlook, however, is far from bleak. As implied in the introduction, awareness is the key to change. It may be painful to take such a long, hard look at ourselves, but somewhere deep inside, we all know it must be done.

Nasty tasting medicine is sometimes the first step on the road to recovery.

Chapter Thirteen

We Are Motivated And Manipulated By Guilt
(Just Say "No!")

It is common knowledge that if you want to get something from someone who may be reluctant to give it, it is always best to aim for the soft spot in their hearts. Child abductors know this better than anyone. They know that most children have been warned not to talk to strangers and not to trust anyone they don't know. That is why puppy dogs work so well as ploys to gain the sympathy and trust of children. It has been demonstrated time after time that even the most well trained children will sometimes go off with a complete stranger if he/she engages them to help find a lost puppy dog.

So it is with hospital administration and nurses. They know that nurses respond to guilt as naturally as children respond to lost puppies. The hospital then uses this realization to their greatest advantage.

How many times have you answered the phone on your day off only to hear the staffing office begging you to come in and work a few hours. Often these phone calls occur at five or six in the morning, and they never apologize for waking you at such an ungodly hour. They use ploys like telling you that three of your co-workers called out sick today and they just don't know what they're going to do for staffing. If this doesn't work, they go on to tell you how *sick* the patients are and that you are one of the only people whom they know can handle this critical situation.

They usually wrap it up with a line like, "So, what do you say? Can you come in and help us out?"

If you succumb to the guilt and say "yes" (we've all done it at one time or another), you win approximately five minutes of your supervisor's approval. If you decide that you'd rather walk barefoot over hot coals than go in and tell them "no," you will hear a distinct and angry "click" in your ear as they hang up the phone and try the next victim. What's interesting is how quickly someone who has just been groveling at your feet can suddenly turn on you and cut you off as if you hadn't mattered in the first place.

Furthermore, when they are still begging and groveling for your agreement to come in and work, frequently they act as if you would be doing them a tremendous "favor" by gracing them with your presence. When one person asks a "favor" of another, it usually implies a two way street and the other person eventually gets to receive a "favor" in return. When was the last time a hospital ever considered doing a "favor" for *you*? When was the last time you even considered *asking* them to return any of the multiple "favors" you have done for them? Probably never, since we are usually too guilt-ridden to expect any kind of compensation from an organization that already has so many problems.

Then there is the matter of coming to work when you are sick yourself but too guilt-ridden to stay home where you belong. This seems to be a common syndrome among nurses. More than likely, the reason we get sick is because we are run down from working long hours and rotating shifts short handed. Somehow we've gotten the message that we're not *allowed* to be sick and if we come to work no matter what, we may be miserable, but at least we won't have to feel guilty.

Sometimes when even *we* recognize that it would serve no one for us to come to work when we are ill, we still feel obliged to sound *really sick* over the telephone when we call the staffing office. We are only playing along in this game of manipulation when we do this. We are health care professionals and obviously have the judgment to know when we are too ill to work. We only insult ourselves and destroy our dignity when we try to prove how ill we are by trying to "sound sick" over the telephone. If our best judgment is good enough for ourselves and our patients, it should be good enough for the staffing office.

Another area where we seek approval and allow ourselves to be manipulated by guilt is on our annual performance evaluations. It seems rather interesting (not to mention a little dysfunctional), that the person who judges every staff nurse on every shift on the unit spends most of her/his time on only the day shift and usually in meetings that are in some remote area of the hospital, far away from the nurses and their patients. One has to wonder (but would dare not ask, for fear of receiving a poor evaluation), how someone who has never witnessed first hand what the staff nurse actually does can possibly evaluate that nurse on her so-called "performance."

Also, it is not uncommon for a staff nurse to be given an evaluation that rates her somewhat below her actual level. Generally the nurse is told that her performance is actually better than what is reflected on the evaluation, but that if the supervisor rated her as superior, she would have nothing to "aim" for. In other words, a nurse -- just because she *is* a nurse -- can never be considered excellent, superior or superb in her job. Furthermore, we are often given "goals" to aim for by the time of our next evaluation. This is one more way of trying to motivate and manipulate us with guilt over the fact that we just are not good enough the way we are. It is one more tactic we let the system use in order to keep us feeling inadequate and seeking their approval.

It sometimes seems our capacity for guilt is a bottomless well. In addition to the insidious, daily manipulation of nurses through the use of guilt, there are some even more blatant examples. Natural disasters are a perfect culture media for our "guilt receptors."

A vicious and unexpected storm once slammed into several small towns along the eastern seaboard. Coastal communities were walloped and hundreds of people suffered from exposure to the icy December winds as an angry and violent ocean flooded homes, knocking out power lines, telephones and heat. Most people had to be rescued and evacuated by the National Guard and many were brought to the local hospital to be treated for everything from minor cuts and bruises to exposure and shock.

A nurse who lived in that community watched in horror as she saw her car shoved into the nearby river by the ocean waves. She packed a small knapsack and waited anxiously for the National Guard to rescue her, as she watched the water in her yard rise up over the porch steps and eventually seep into her living room.

The nurse was rescued and brought to an emergency shelter, where a friend picked her up and brought her to his home several miles inland. Still shivering, and realizing that she only had the clothes on her back and the few essentials she had packed in her knapsack, the nurse called the hospital to let them know she would not be in for her shift tonight.

Immediately and unsympathetically she was asked, "And just why not?"

The nurse was flabbergasted, but gave them the benefit of the doubt. She explained that she lived in the community that had just been destroyed by the ocean. She tried her best not to cry as she added that she had lost everything, including her car that now sat at the bottom of the river.

"Well, that's no problem" she was told. "We'll send security out to pick you up and bring you in to work."

"But I don't even have any clothes!" the nurse insisted, horrified at the callused attitude of the nursing supervisor.

She was then told that the hospital would provide her with O.R. greens to wear, even though it was against hospital policy for med/surg nurses to wear scrubs to work. The supervisor told the nurse to "pull herself together" because "these poor people need her right now," and that the security van would pick her up in an hour, "so please be ready."

Even though the nurse had been one of the hardest hit victims of the storm, she was expected to put her own needs and feelings on hold as she catered to the needs of the hospital, which was staffed adequately with nurses who lived farther inland. Simply because she had no physical injuries she could flaunt, her state of mind was considered insignificant. The icing on the cake came when the nurse broke down at work and began crying over her losses and was reprimanded for her "inappropriate" behavior.

As a profession, we have proven that we are susceptible to guilt and will break our backs (sometimes literally), to gain our employers' approval. We are only too willing to carry the burden of poor planning, etc., rather than let the parties responsible (usually the staffing office), pay the consequences for their actions.

It is important to realize that nurses don't have to continue to be controlled and ruled by guilt. In all of the previous examples, every one of the nurses could have stopped the guilt cycle by simply saying "No!" "No!" to guilt-induced overtime. "No!" to having to justify being sick. "No!" to inaccurate and manipulative performance evaluations (refuse to sign such an insult!) and especially "No!" to disregarding our own health and well being for the unrealistic demands of the hospital.

Chapter Fourteen

We Try To Raise Our Self Esteem In All The Wrong Ways

Tom Foolery, M.D. The title demands respect in spite of the ridiculous name. Tom Foolery will never have a self esteem problem as long as he has that "M.D." after his name. Those two letters say it all.

Now take a look at some other names you might see on any given day in the health care field. Nancy Jones, R.N., B.S.N.; Susan Healy, M.A., R.N.; Judy Smith, M.S.N., R.N., CCRN; Patricia O'Brien, Ph.D., R.N., F.A.A.N.; Janet Walsh, Ed.D., R.N., CCRN, F.A.A.N. Get the picture yet?

It's a lot like that syndrome we see with short men. Often, they tend to speak more loudly than necessary, feel compelled to flaunt their accomplishments, and constantly want to be in the spotlight. Those of us who remember anything from our "Abnormal Psych" courses know that this is just their way of overcompensating for an underlying feeling of inadequacy. Perhaps it's time to take a long, hard look at ourselves.

Many people with an "M.D." after their names, have several more degrees and initials they could easily add to their list, but most choose to go with the "M.D." only. A wise choice. They know they have nothing to prove to anyone, and they understand that putting the entire alphabet after your name just seems a little too much like begging for acceptance. And skilled, educated professionals should never have to beg for acceptance.

We in the nursing profession, however, seem to have something to prove, especially to ourselves. Yes, education is a wonderful thing and nurses should and do have lots of it. That's a given. So why don't we let that "R.N." say it all for us the way the "M.D." says it all for physicians? Is it because the nursing profession has so many different entry levels that the general public, and even some branches of the medical profession, aren't exactly sure what "R.N." means? Are these different entry levels of nursing one more way to keep us divided and powerless as a group? Granted, the world (especially the medical world), does not seem to want to give the title "R.N." the respect it deserves, but is adding a lengthy series of initials to our names really going to change that? Perhaps we would we be better off by deciding on only *one* entry level for nurses, thereby making the initials "RN" less confusing than they are now, and as readily understood as the initials, "M.D.".

Speaking of educational levels, there has been a civil war going on within our profession over what the minimal educational requirements should be for that coveted "R.N.". Should it require a minimum of a two, three, or four year degree? An interesting thought to ponder at this point is that when someone is a great artist or musician or athlete, no one looks for any type of degree to verify their ability. Instead, their raw talent is so apparent that they don't need to prove a thing. Nursing was an art long before it was a science, and it certainly takes an undeniable *raw talent* to be a nurse. So why are we the only "artists" who have no credibility without a long list of letters after our names?

Think about a person who grew up in poverty, then suddenly comes into a windfall of cash. Maybe they won the lottery or came into an unexpected inheritance. These are the people who will immediately go for the flashy car, the lavish clothes, and the ornately decorated home. They are announcing to the world that they count now. Next, look at a person who comes from "old money." You can pick them out simply by their demeanor. Even if you catch them in jeans and a T-shirt, doing their gardening with a smudge of soil on their nose, they still ooze a sense of sophistication and refinement. There is no doubt that they are someone special.

That is how it should be in nursing. We shouldn't have to *flaunt* our degrees and skills in order to prove that we have them. Instead, we should know deep in the center of our being that we deserve respect and then act accordingly. An aura of dignity and self respect will go a lot farther than a long list of initials after our names. Rich people have always understood this.

If the series of letters after our names isn't enough, we have also devised job titles which we erroneously believe will bring us the respect we so desperately crave. What the heck is a "Nurse Manager?" Someone who manages nurses (those highly skilled and educated people with all the initials after their names)? Granted, there are times when a nurse may need to consult with a colleague, but do we ever need someone to *manage* us? No wonder our egos are so battered and bruised!

We complain that no one understands what exactly it is we do, and perhaps that is because the answer is such a complicated and intricate one. But then we further complicate these confused non-nurses by giving ourselves titles like "team leader," "Clinical Nurse II," "charge nurse", "senior nurse," and "nurse educator." Can we really be offended if they laugh? Isn't this really just another way to keep us divided?

Actually, the "Clinical Ladders" concept, where a nurse is "rewarded" for her expertise at the bedside, is a very insulting and unhealthy scheme to implement in an already divided group. First of all, anyone who does *not* have "bedside expertise," should not be in nursing. Secondly, the so-called "reward" for increasing one's expertise adds up to only nickels and dimes, yet encourages people to sacrifice themselves to outdo each other for promotion and status. We are constantly being told we are a team, but then are infused with a spirit of competitiveness where one team member is rewarded at the expense of another. This is one more tactic used to make a mockery of our status and to prevent us from uniting and becoming powerful.

That brings us to the subject of "nursing diagnosis." The people who dreamed up and promote nursing diagnosis say that it's a way to elevate our profession. Any nurse in the real world, however, who works with real patients and real illnesses, knows that the only thing "nursing diagnosis" accomplishes is keeping us away from our patients who so desperately need us. Why would anyone think this was a good way to elevate our profession? Can you think of any profession that would welcome more paperwork and "busy work" as a way of proving their worth?

Again, we seem to be suffering from low self esteem here.

Why isn't it enough to be a nurse? What is so wrong or lowly about the skills, nurturing and caring, we give to our patients? Why are they trying to make us look like "junior doctors" instead of the healers, nurturers, and miracle workers that we are? Most of all, why would anyone even think we need to "elevate" our profession? There is nothing wrong with our profession, it's our self esteem that needs elevating. And trying to imitate physicians is not the way to do it.

Paying us more money would be an effective way of elevating our self esteem, but for some reason, no one has suggested that one yet. Including our input in policy making decisions would help too. In fact, the list is endless.

This is not to suggest that we are poor helpless victims of the system. Oh, no. We have played a major role in putting ourselves in this position. Have you ever noticed the way abused children often cling to the monstrous parent who batters them? They resist the foreign feeling of a new and safer home and cling instead to what is familiar, even if it hurts, even if it eventually kills them. They have known nothing but abuse and their self esteem is as battered as their little bodies. That is similar to what we have done as a profession. We cling to our abusers as though we have no choices. But we are adults, educated and intelligent adults, and if we don't find an effective way to raise our low self esteem, we are never going to change the balance of power to make it work for us.

All the initials in the world, all the grandiose titles we can dream up, and all the copycat behaviors we can emulate, will never replace what is missing at the very core of our profession: a staunch belief in our own worthiness.

Break out the self help books if you must, but let's stop spinning our wheels and wasting our time and energy on pathetic and ineffective ways of raising our low self esteem. The real process of recovery begins in the heart of every individual nurse as she/he begins to treat her/himself and her/his colleagues with respect and dignity ... and expects nothing less in return.

Chapter Fifteen

We Are Pathetically Grateful For Meaningless Tokens Of Appreciation
(Of Lollipops and Condoms)

Nurses are no slouches when it comes to dealing with insults. We get plenty of practice every time a physician decides to have a temper tantrum, or a demented patient tries to humiliate us, or an irate visitor loudly demands to speak to the supervisor. But of all the indignities we must endure, none is as insulting as the senseless and offensive "gifts" nurses receive on "Nurse's Day" from our hospital administrators.

Nurses in various hospitals around the country have received everything from party favors to coffee mugs to giant lollipops with a hole in the middle and the slogan "You Are Our Lifesavers" imprinted on them. Perhaps the most insulting gift of all, however, was a hospital that gave out *condoms*, yes, condoms, to its nurses. How do you even respond to an insult like that? Obviously, we have a long way to go.

That there is any such thing as "National Recognition Day for Nurses," is seen as an insult by many nurses. The concept itself isn't really a bad idea, but the delivery is sorely lacking. Most nurses would gladly trade in their trinkets and ice cream sundaes that hospital administration so generously doles out to them on that day in return for some *real* appreciation. Real appreciation might include things like, adequate staffing, appropriate monetary compensation, and two way communication with administration instead of the impersonal, one way street that exists in most hospitals. Of course, the most meaningful token of appreciation might be treating nurses with the same regard and esteem reserved solely for physicians and hospital administrators.

To simply designate one day as "Nurse Appreciation Day" or any other meaningless title they want to give it, is just too *easy*. Often it turns out to be nothing more than lip service and hospitals usually don't even do a good job of *that*. Can you imagine a "Lawyer's Day" or a "CEO's Day"? To humor us with such patronizing "gifts" demonstrates nothing more than the institution's lack of commitment to nurses, the largest and most crucial department in any hospital.

"Nurse's Day" is not the only example of silly and senseless tokens of appreciation, but it is the most obvious. Take a look around any hospital and you will see several more subtle and insincere attempts at making us feel valued, but which leave us feeling degraded instead.

Many hospitals reserve a parking place in one of the prime parking lots with a sign that reads, "Reserved for Employee of the Month." Doesn't this erode any sense of professionalism and dignity that we have achieved? Look at the reverse psychology being used here. The hospital expects us to compete for the opportunity to have convenient parking for one month. This is an easy way to distract us from the real issue, which is that every one of us should have convenient parking *everyday*.

The gratuitous room designated as "The Nurse's Lounge" is another example of this meaningless tokenism. When was the last time you saw nurses lounging while on duty? Usually these so-called "lounges" are used instead for storage of equipment, or any number of purposes, none of which include "lounging."

Many hospitals also host an annual awards dinner for nurses who have been employed by the institution for a particular amount of time, usually in five year increments. The nurse's name is called as she steps up to receive a small, gold-plated pin (that she would be too embarrassed to actually wear), from a smiling administrator who, if he passed her in the hall the next day, wouldn't know her.

One has to wonder what is the real purpose of these condescending and embarrassing gestures. Is it to distract us from the *real* issues of money and adequate staffing? Is it a tactic to diffuse our anger at all of the indignities and injustices we endure at the hands of a system that has no genuine regard for its nurses? Talk is cheap, and so are green lollipops, condoms, and gold-plated pins. Somehow hospitals always seem to find money for the things they are *committed* to, like decorating the lobby or creating more office space. Apparently, the adequate compensation of nurses is not something to which they are committed.

Even the penal system in this country has a better "reward" system than most nurses receive. Convicted rapists and felons receive *meaningful* rewards, like time off for good behavior, early parole, and opportunities to improve their circumstances. These are rewards that *count*! You don't see an asinine idea like "Prisoner's Day," because, if you did, you would also see an uprising.

Think about it. We get a cheap, silly little pin for "serving" five years, while hard core criminals receive significant opportunities for their efforts. Where is the logic here? They serve *time*, we serve *mankind.*

Unfortunately, many nurses are only too willing to give their hospitals the benefit of the doubt. Instead of voicing their opinions and refusing to participate in these degrading events, they accept these insulting gestures and say (as if it were a mantra), "Well, at least it's *something.*"

But it's not *something*! In fact, it is less than *nothing.* "Something" would be including nurses in the decision making loop of the hospital. "Something" would be providing us with the basic equipment and adequate staffing we need. "Something" would be a continuous recognition of our importance, not just lip service on one specified day.

An experienced nurse once made an appointment with an administrator in her hospital to discuss an ongoing problem to which she thought she had a solution. The administrator told her the idea would never work (but later used the idea and took credit for it as his own). Sensing the nurse's frustration and recognizing her creative potential, he asked her to join one of the many committees where issues such as this were discussed. The nurse was only too happy to be included in a system where she felt her ideas would be heard -- that is, until she was informed that she would not be *paid* for her time.

Who but a nurse would put up with this? Anyone else who had the experience and creative potential of this nurse would call themselves a "consultant" and the hospital would gladly pay large sums of money for their expertise. Sadly, nurses will leave no stone unturned when it comes to getting their patients' needs fulfilled, but we seem to have a very hard time demanding the same for ourselves. Time after time we allow the hospitals to use money as an excuse for not following through with our suggestions, and we try not to notice the opulence that is displayed when it comes to *their* own well-being.

Nurses are an amazing paradox. We have the strongest egos in the world because we are able to let most of the insults we endure simply roll off our backs as we calmly trudge through our shifts, doing our very best for everyone. We also have the weakest egos in the world because we quietly accept outright abuse and rarely, if ever, fight back.

The only way for us to reverse our situation is to first recognize the absurdity of these meaningless tokens of appreciation, and second, to refuse to participate in our own demise any longer.

Chapter Sixteen

We Accept Accountability For Everyone's Actions, Mistakes And Work (Establish Some Boundaries!)

In any profession, the issue of accountability is a serious matter. In a profession that involves the care, well-being, safety, and comfort of other people, accountability is a continuos priority and concern. Nurses understand the concept of being responsible for one's work and actions. We are taught to be accountable for our actions from the first day of nursing school onward.

Nurses accept that facet of their profession willingly. In fact, we have learned the lessons of accountability so well we often find ourselves extending our personal accountability to include the actions of others. What we so easily lose sight of is the fact that accountably is a two way street. We have the right as professionals to hold others accountable for their actions. Unfortunately, we rarely exercise this right.

What happens instead is that we find ourselves instinctively accepting accountability and responsibility for everything that goes on around us. Our accountability all too often has a *global* quality that can become counter-productive and self-damaging.

Some of us seem eager and more than willing to operate in this way because we have been duped into believing that we are "special" or more "dependable" in some way by a manager or co-worker. Thus, we should offer ourselves up to be held accountable for the work and actions of, not only ourselves, but everyone else we work with. We are conditioned to instantly put our necks on the block when there is a problem; it's simply second nature. Some nurses do it to score "points" with superiors because it was drilled into their heads that accepting accountability for everything that happens is what a *professional* should do.

Still other nurses do it simply because accepting blame and criticism has become a way of life. They don't think much about it. The self-esteem of these nurses is so damaged they are certain that when something doesn't go right, they made the mistake. Being a whipping-post is second nature. Their confidence in their own nursing skills and expertise is so low they simply don't think other people can make mistakes.

Right about here, your internalized nurse is probably kicking and screaming. She may be telling you to take this book and burn it as heresy. Fair enough. It's a free world. No one is suggesting that accountability isn't an important issue. We must be accountable for our own work and our actions. We must be accountable for those persons we supervise and direct. However, if you can get her to calm down for a moment and think clearly, ask yourself these questions. Your answers just may surprise you.

How many times during an eight hour work day do you say *you are sorry for something*? How many times do you say the words, *"I'm sorry but...."* to a patient or a member of the patient's family, a physician, or a manager.

Think about this. Take a moment and consider your typical work day.

How many times a day do you *apologize* for something not

done properly by someone else? How often throughout your day do you make excuses for the actions of others? How frequently do you find yourself explaining to a patient why they don't have something that they certainly should have, even though the problem wasn't your fault? If your answer is all the time, you are not alone.

Nurses consistently, at times almost compulsively, accept and shoulder the responsibility and blame for other people's actions. We are often the first to excuse inappropriate behavior on the part of physicians and co-workers; we shield co-workers who have poor work habits by "taking up the slack" and doing their work as well as our own; we accept tardiness, ineptness and downright laziness on the part of other staff members and employees.

We rarely speak up about what is *really* going on because our main goal is to get the work done, take care of the patients and simply survive the day. Nurses are trained to keep the work flowing and make sure that all tasks are eventually done properly. We are conditioned and expected to do this regardless of who was truly responsible for the problem. How many times have you heard, "Well, you are the nurse. It's your job to fix it"?

Consider for a moment the people you work with on a daily basis. Take an honest look at your co-worker's personality, styles, and habits. When a problem arises how do they respond? Do they suddenly "disappear"? Do they respond with hostility? Do they remain silent when questions are asked concerning a problem and how the problem came about? Do they quickly find something urgent to do when it comes time to solve the problem or explain what happened? Do they throw their hands up and act helpless, overwhelmed or totally unaware that there is a problem? The odds are excellent that these are the responses many of your co-workers exhibit on a daily basis.

Now, take a moment and consider how most nurses respond in these situations. Think about how you respond when problems arise. First, the nurse looks for a solution. Then, if you examine situations honestly, you will find that is usually the nurse who makes excuses for others. It is the nurse who takes the role of peace keeper in situations where there is conflict. Most often, it is the nurse who makes the effort to "smooth over" the rough spots created by other people. Nurses rarely confront the person who is truly responsible for the shortcoming or problem. We fail to speak up even when we find ourselves taking the heat, absorbing the hostility, and facing the consequences for other people's mistakes or short comings.

We don't even bat an eye. We just stand there and take it. We do it automatically. We do it without thinking about the effect it has on our self-esteem, both as a professional and as a person. We do it without considering the costs to our professional image. So, why do we do this? We do it simply because we are nurses. It is the nurse who is supposed to be accountable for all things and all people, all the time, right? Wrong.

So why shouldn't we do this? Because it is unrealistic, unprofessional, and does us tremendous harm as professional nurses and human beings. It erodes our self-respect. It causes us to minimize the tremendous amount of excellent work that we do. It saps our energy and makes us look inadequate in the eyes of patients and others. It sends all the wrong messages about who we are and what kind of nurse we want to be. It raises our stress levels, making us feel frustrated and resentful. Eventually, it contributes to professional burn-out and emotional exhaustion. Without established boundaries, our tendency to accept global accountability simply runs amok.

A nurse who works in an outpatient clinical setting told me this story. One of her assigned responsibilities was to take "sick calls" from her staff. When a staff member was ill and needed to call in sick, they called this nurse. It was her responsibility to then arrange for alternate staff coverage. When it came time for her to take an advance-planned, well earned week of vacation, she felt she had to arrange a way to continue taking "sick call" even while on vacation in another state. Her plan was certainly encouraged by her manager and co-workers. No one else wanted to be responsible for this duty.

Her plan was to leave her answering machine on while she was away. Then, every morning while on vacation she would set her alarm for 6:00 a.m. and call her machine using her personal code to get her messages. She would then know if anyone was going to miss work that day. If someone happened to call in sick, she would call other staff members from her hotel and arrange coverage. The long distance phone calls would be at her expense.

Well, like all the best laid plans, this one went haywire. It so happened that, indeed, one of the staff called in sick. Unfortunately, a friend who was house-sitting for the nurse forgot about the arrangement and answered the phone when the sick staff member called. Upon hearing a strange voice answering the nurse's phone, she hung up without giving her name or message. Not having the phone number of the manager or an alternate, she did not report her impending absence at work until it was too late to find a replacement.

Upon returning to work on her first day back from vacation, the nurse's manager pulled her into her office and reprimanded her for causing a major disruption in staffing while on vacation. Needless to say, the nurse's vacation was retroactively ruined by all the stress and blame she experienced over this incident. She was also told that the entire clinic had "gone to hell in a hand basket" because of her absence. So, where did this very conscientious, well meaning nurse go wrong? And how did her "work system" help her get there?

This nurse's story is an example of how easy it is for us to assume global and continuous responsibility for our work situations under inappropriate conditions. It is not rational, acceptable, or necessary for us to be expected or required to assume global responsibility for the actions of others when we are on vacation, home sick, or away from our jobs for other reasons.

It is our responsibility and the responsibility of managers and co-workers to prepare and plan in advance for coverage during an absence. Nurses are accustomed to rotating vacation time, working to cover for absent co-workers, taking turns working on holidays, and making sure that coverage is provided. However, we should not hold ourselves responsible or allow others to hold us accountable for the actions of others or for problems that arise in our absence. That isn't to say this is easy to accomplish when co-workers and managers attempt to make us feel guilty of "abandonment" before we even take our vacation. The point, is we should not allow this to happen. It is manipulative, disrespectful, and demeaning behavior. We have a right to refuse and denounce this type of treatment.

How many times have you felt guilty for taking a well-earned, advanced approved vacation? How many times have you actually felt like a prisoner released on temporary parole when you went on vacation? How many times have you been tempted to "check in" with work while on vacation? How many times did you actually do it? And if you did "check in," how did it make you feel? Probably not very good.

This chapter began with some tough questions. And so, it seems fitting that it should end with one more. When thinking about your "accountability style" ask yourself one thing: where does your personal and professional accountability begin and where does it end? If you have the resolve to answer this important question, you will increase your awareness and strengthen your professional image. The result will be that you will learn to be truly accountable to yourself for your professional and personal well-being. Establishing your boundaries and operating from within your appropriate field of accountability will strengthen you as a professional. It will enable you to reclaim your focus, and thus your power, as a professional nurse.

Chapter Seventeen

We Don't Build Relationships Among Ourselves

The parents of a police officer were driving on the freeway when, suddenly their car made a funny noise and conked out completely on the shoulder of the road. A State Trooper happened to be passing by and stopped to assist the couple. He called a tow truck for them and waited with them for its arrival. When the tow truck arrived, it was quickly determined that the car could not be fixed at the roadside and needed to be towed to the local service station fifty miles from the couple's home.

Upon mentioning that their son was a police officer, the State Trooper put them in his car and drove them to the boundary of his "territory." He then radioed for another trooper from the neighboring "territory," who showed up within minutes. The second trooper put the couple in his car and drove them right to their door. During the drive, they all had a pleasant conversation about the couple's son, who was a New York City police officer.

As the trooper pulled into the driveway, the couple thanked him profusely for his kindness. The trooper just smiled and answered, "Hey, you're family."

Nurses could learn an awful lot from the incredible camaraderie that exists in the law enforcement profession. Police understand, perhaps better than anyone else, what tremendous strength there is in fellowship. Have you ever seen what happens when they hear over their radios that a "brother" or "sister" officer needs assistance? Every available officer drops whatever he/she is doing and all but flies to the aid of their fellow officer. Personal differences are forgotten, and every officer puts the welfare of their brother or sister officer above all else. Is it any wonder that even the most hardened criminals hesitate to assault a cop? They know that, if they do, they will face the wrath of the entire police force and that, at least, makes them think twice. If unity like this can intimidate criminals, think what it could do for the nursing profession!

Can you imagine how much power nurses would have if we developed the kind of loyalty to one another that the cops have? Can you imagine what would happen if, we stopped bickering among ourselves and started supporting one another? There would be no limit to our power!

Sadly, we are doing exactly what every hospital administrator wants us to do: wasting so much time and energy fighting among ourselves that we don't have the stamina to confront the real issues. How many times have you argued with a "fellow" nurse over the phone when she is trying to send you your fourth admission of the night from the emergency room? Chances are you don't even *know* her, and chances are excellent that this is not a personal vendetta on her part, but rather a result of the pressure the system is putting on her to clear the emergency room.

Unfortunately, nurses work in such high stress situations on a daily basis that, much like any oppressed people, the very predictable result is often horizontal violence. Also, like most oppressed people, nurses have an underlying attitude of scarcity rather than abundance. We are always afraid there won't be enough.

Enough time. Enough help. Enough supplies. Enough anything. So we bicker, blame and accuse one another of being the enemy when, in fact, we wouldn't know the real enemy if we sat on it.

In nursing, our biggest enemy is the way we isolate ourselves from one another. We don't bother to form meaningful bonds with each other; we don't have calm or rational conversations with each other about where the system is failing us and our patients. Coming up with a creative solution to a "systems" problem, is the one job no one wants us to have for fear we will realize it is not we who are at fault, but the horrendous conditions under which we work.

Instead, we do terrible things to each other: we criticize one another, we gossip about each other: we try to out do each other: we write each other up. Can you imagine how happy this makes the hospital administration? As long as we are fighting and isolating ourselves from one another, it is only too easy to keep us "in our place."

A "Nurse Manager" once called her staff into a meeting to discuss the nurses' "inefficiency" in accepting patients from the P.A.C.U. The nurses in the P.A.C.U. had apparently kept a record for three months of how many minutes they were kept waiting to give report to the floor nurses who were receiving their patients. They then presented a list of how many minutes of their time the floor nurses had "wasted." Did they really think this was going to accomplish anything besides further alienating themselves from the med/surg nurses they worked with everyday? They would have accomplished far more with twenty minutes of honest conversation and brainstorming between the two units and presenting a united front to the administration, insisting on the implementation of what they saw as a solution. Instead, they spent three months pointing the finger at and undermining their colleagues. When will we ever learn?

Nurses will only be empowered through the cooperation of large numbers of us. One of our most serious misjudgments, has been thinking that the best way we have of managing important nursing issues is located "out there," at the level of state or national nursing organizations. Nothing could be farther from the truth, and if you don't believe it, just look at the cops again. They support each other on issues that affect them as a whole, no matter what their personal differences. We need to do the same thing. Some of the most serious and important issues of nursing practice can only be resolved by nurses cooperating together on their units.

In addition to finding creative solutions to our common concerns, the mere fact that we would support each other and show real loyalty toward each other is a very empowering tactic. There is probably no more touching scene, or no more accurate picture of the strength of this type of camaraderie than when police officers mourn the death of one of their fellow officers. You will see police uniforms, even from different towns or precincts, for as far as the eye can see. They will organize themselves and step up to the casket in groups of two or three, stand at attention, and salute their fallen "brother." They will be there for the families of the officer and there is nothing they won't do to show respect for that officer, whether they knew him or not.

When have you ever seen nurses unite like this in a show of strength and commitment to a common cause? Probably never. Just because we haven't done it yet, though, doesn't mean we can't do it in the future. The change must start subtly, in the hearts of individual nurses who begin to cooperate with one another on their units. Little by little, others will become enlightened and, before you know it, nursing would be a powerful sisterhood that *finally* looks after its own welfare. And not a minute too soon.

Chapter Eighteen

We Fail To Align Ourselves With The Public Through Information And Education
(Become A Healthcare Consumer Advocate!)

Nurses are trained to be patient advocates. As nurses, we generally focus our efforts and attention on the *individual patient*. We then extend our scope of practice to include the patient's immediate circle of spouse, family, and closest friends. Our role in relation to the patient includes that of caregiver, protector, nurturer, and advocate. Because we are part of the health care system, we sometimes suffer from tunnel vision when we think of our patients only as *patients.* That same "tunnel vision" bonds us together exclusively as *patient* and *nurse.* However, this very special relationship needs to be broadened so that both nurses and patients reap the benefits.

You might be wondering what is wrong with thinking about the people we care for strictly as patients. In terms of delivering the care the person needs, there is absolutely nothing wrong with viewing that person strictly as a patient. However, in terms of promoting the nursing profession and educating the public about what nurses do and about the changes needed within the health care system, we need to also view the patient as part of a larger group called the *public.*

More importantly, we need to view our patients as *powerful, active participants of the public* who should be educated about the important role nurses play in their lives and in the health of our country. In addition, *we should extend our scope of advocacy* to include not only the patient, but the public as well. We automatically think of ourselves as patient advocates, but we tend to stop there. We should be looking at the bigger picture and aim to be public advocates as well.

Nurses as advocates of the public will be required to assume a more active, independent role to educate and inform the public about nursing within the context of our health care system. As public activists and advocates, we are free to bring up questions about the quality of care the public should expect from their health care system and providers. We can educate and inform the public about safety issues in hospitals. We can inform the patient about how the health care system is run, who is running it, and what the problems are from a nursing perspective. Serving as a public advocate requires an active, independent, and positive voice. So, how does this differ from being a *patient* advocate?

To better understand this question, consider the different connotations that are attached to the role of *patient*. Usually, patients are assigned and accept a more *passive* role within the health care system. The patient is the *passive recipient* of nursing and medical care. When a person is in the passive role of patient, he or she ceases to exist in any other capacity. The patient role is well defined and well orchestrated. Therefore, the type of advocacy we practice towards a patient is also going to be more passive and well defined because of the restrictive nature of the health care system. That doesn't necessarily mean that we must assume a passive stance when it comes to our patients. It simply means that, as patient advocates, we are working within the context of a given system.

We are usually employees of the system and as such, dependent on that system for our jobs and income. Our position as employees within the system, plus the patient's passive role as the same system, limits what we can do as the patient's advocate. It shouldn't be this way, but that is the reality that nurses must face on a daily basis. Nurses often feel as powerless as their patients seem to be. And yet, are *nurses* and *patients* truly powerless? In our frustration with the current status of our standing within the health care system, it often seems so.

After all, patients do not make decisions about such things as how we practice, or under what conditions we are told to practice, how the system is managed, or how nursing salaries are determined. Perhaps they should be. More importantly, *patients* are never informed about how these decisions are made or by whom. We have been taught that *to tell a patient* you won't be able to tend to his or her needs immediately because you have been assigned ten other sick patients for your shift is unethical. We have been trained *never to tell a patient* that nursing care is critically low because the hospital didn't schedule enough nurses.

We would be severely reprimanded if we told a *family member of a patient* that their loved one wasn't receiving the appropriate critical nursing care because the patient was on a busy ward instead of being in the intensive care unit where the patient belonged in the first place. Because we are strong patient advocates, we do these things anyway, and deal with the consequences later. (We keep the unpleasant "consequences" from the patient also.)

Patients are to be protected from what really goes on in hospitals and other health care facilities. So goes the party line of adminstrative dogma. *Patients are not to be told* of dangerous working conditions, inadequate staffing, cost cutting measures that jeopardize patient care and safety, or mistakes made due to fatigue and stress on the part of a nurse who is simply stretched too thinly between patients. (Besides, the adminstrative finger of fault will point directly at a nurse.)

In fact, nurses are expected to keep the *patient* well shielded from these nasty little secrets. Nurses are expected to participate in this dangerous game of shielding the *patient* from the realities of our working conditions. We are expected to carry on and maintain an air of caring, competency, and above all else, keep everything working. On top of that, we are expected to assure the patient that no where else would the patient get such wonderful care, even though this may be blatantly untrue. To add insult to injury, we are expected to smile and give the patient the impression that we are extremely well treated and generously compensated by our employer.

Nurses are expected to *"make do"* the best they can, carry on against any odds, and ration nursing care among the sickest patients, but never let the patient know the true state of affairs outside their rooms. Nurses are expected to plug up the holes in the dike and hope to God the flood waters can be contained, at least until their shift is over. After all, it is the *nurse* who is ultimately responsible for that patient's care. Therefore, if something goes wrong with that patient, it is the nurse who is at fault. Right? It is the *nurse* who didn't run fast enough from patient to patient. It's the *nurse* who didn't assess the patient frequently enough. It is the *nurse* who suffers from guilt and feelings of inadequacy, frustration, and sheer anger when patients don't receive the appropriate nursing care. It's the *nurse* who leaves her patients at the end of her eight to twelve hours and drives home thinking of twenty things she should have done for her patients but simply didn't have the time to do.

We in the health field often fail to recognize that our patients are also part of the public. We even seem to forget that nurses are also part of the powerful force called the public and, as such, have the same rights, privileges, and power as anyone else when it comes to asking tough questions and demanding answers. Acting on behalf of a patient and practicing advocacy for our patients within a health care setting is an important function of nurses. However, *practicing as a public advocate* takes us into a different arena. The nursing profession has a rich heritage when it comes to the role of public advocacy. Our voices have been raised and heard in the past and changes occurred. The public needs to hear from us once again. So, how do we go about this?

One of the first steps in practicing as a public advocate is to recognize we are experts at what we do. We have expertise, information, ideas, and experience that can benefit the *public.* In addition, the problems within the health care system that nurses face are not just our problems; They are also part of the *public's domain*. In many instances, our problems involve *public safety issues*. For nurses and patients, these problems are "up close and personal." We often, we know exactly what needs to be done and how to get it done.

However, we can't expect them to support our efforts for change if we don't inform and educate the public about the problems that nurses face every working day. If the public is shielded, protected, and looked upon as a passive recipient of our nursing practice, they cannot join us in changing the system within which we all exist. Nurses can no longer allow themselves to be forced into being co-conspirators with the health care system.

The public has a right to know about what is really going on in hospitals when it comes to nursing practice. The stakes are high. Our careers are on the line. The essence of nursing is hanging in the balance. The stakes are even higher for our patients. Their lives are dependent on our ability to practice nursing and to do so with adequate staffing and work conditions.

No longer can we keep the "secrets" about what is happening to nurses in this country's health care system. If we continue to allow our nursing practice to be defined, determined, limited and censored by health care administrations, it will be nurses, patients, and the public who suffer the consequences.

Many professions and service industries outside health care already have learned that the public has immense power and influence. When educated and given the facts, the public can be a powerful source of change and innovation. Other professions realize that the best way to insure job security is by making their customers/clients/consumer aware of the services and products they can offer them. Other professions know the power of aligning with the consumer in order to regulate, overhaul, or monitor an industry or system and bring about needed change.

The consumer holds power simply because they can turn to another source of any product or service and *take their business elsewhere* if they aren't getting what they need. Nurses would be wise to remember that patients are also customers/clients/consumers of the health care system, and as such, can be powerful advocates for nursing when given the means and opportunity. We should take every opportunity to align ourselves with the health care consumer and educate the consumer about how valuable, indispensable, and irreplaceable we are. Informed, educated consumers are powerful consumers and, more importantly, powerful allies.

Nurses can be powerful and effective consumer and public advocates. The public has immense regard and respect for nurses. We should encourage and seek out public recognition and attention. We can do this in our work settings by attending any event that involves the public. Nurses should be *in force* at "open houses", fund raising events, or media coverage events. We don't have to wait for administration to "invite" us. We can't wait for administrations to blow our horns. We should blow our own horns, and blow the whistle on the health care system.

We can seek out health care consumers and the public within our communities. After all, every person we meet or talk with is a health care consumer and potential advocate for nurses. Nurses should join business organizations, Lion's Clubs, Kiwanis Clubs, community outreach programs, church and school organizations. Nurses should do things such as write editorials for local newspapers and articles for magazines, go on television and the radio, or volunteer at health fairs. Nurses, above all else, should be visible and accessible to the public and to the media. What's wrong with a nurse being the keynote speaker for the local Kiwanis Club?

The public and our health care consumers need to hear our stories. We need to make ourselves known to the public as professionals who have something no one else within the health care system can give them. We need to inform and educate our public and consumers about what changes are needed within the system in order for us to provide them with quality nursing care. These things are within the reach of each and every one of us. After all, our public awaits us. We belong in the spot light.

Chapter Nineteen

We Believe We Are Part Of The "Healthcare Team" When We're Not

There is a story about a tribe of natives who live high in the mountain jungles of a distant continent. The tribe is based upon a communal type society, where each member contributes and works for the benefit of the tribe. One such group of workers builds huts. Decisions within the hut building association are supposed to be made according to group consensus and each worker's expertise. Of course, the various tasks involved in building these huts are divided among the workers depending on their special skills.

When someone in the tribe needs a new hut, they go to the hut building association for help. They make their needs known to the hut workers as a group.

Among the hut builders is a special group of workers who produce the grass that is woven and made into the hut roof. This work is highly specialized, and the techniques are passed from one worker to another. Another group of workers are in charge of building the foundation and the structural frame of the hut. The two groups are supposed to work together and be part of the hut building team. However, after many years of working to build the village's huts, the framers began to notice that the roofers seemed to be making all the decisions when it came to building the hut.

In addition, the roofers pocketed the greater portion of the revenue generated by the hut building team. People of the tribe heaped recognition and respect on the roofers. The framers, on the other hand, were a quiet group and went about their work. Besides, they were working so hard and fast, they didn't have much time to complain to the tribe.

In addition, the roofers got most of the perks (more coconut milk, meat, and prestige) than did the framers who had to make do with water, rice, and little recognition for their work. To make matters even more inequitable, it was the roofers who decided the dimensions and design of the huts even though it was the framers who had to then follow the inefficient designs and instructions. The roofers also approved how much building material would be allotted to each hut.

Often, the roofers designed huts that didn't meet the needs of the inhabitant. However, over time, the framers tried to make suggestions, point out design problems, ask for more rice and a little meat, or complained that the building provisions provided by the roofers were inadequate. The roofers responded with hostility. They told the framers to "stick to framing and leave the roofing to the roofers." The roofers told the framers they should be glad they had a job in the first place, and they should make do with what they were given and stop complaining. After all, they were part of the hut building association and everyone had to make sacrifices for the good of the village. When hut owners complained about design problems, the roofers referred the complaints to the framers by saying, "Talk to the framers. They are responsible for that."

As time went by, the framers became more stressed, exhausted, and frustrated. Fewer and fewer people in the village wanted to become a framer. With time, the good framers left the association or died on the job trying to keep up with the roofers' demands.

Gradually, the roofers managed to find reasons to get rid of more and more framers: budget cuts, lack of new huts needing to be built, high cost of materials and such things. Some of the framers were placed in per diem or part time positions. Benefits and salaries continued to be cut.

One year the roofers finally decided that framers just weren't needed anymore. After all, framing wasn't that important, and the job not that complicated. So, the roofers brought in less trained, lower paid Certified Framing Assistants from another tribe and put them to building huts.

The tribe didn't seem too concerned about this as long as they got their huts built, even though a few of the framers tried to warn the tribe about what was happening in the hut building association. The out of work framers tried to warn the tribe of the dangerous situation, but to no avail. The framer's warnings fell on deaf tribal ears.

One year a cook fire was left untended and as a result most of the tribe's huts burned to the ground. There was much crying and hair pulling and general hysteria.

The tribe was suddenly hutless. The tribal leaders went to the hut builders association and asked for help. To their shock and dismay, they found that twenty roofers were available, but that there were no framers left in the entire tribe. Instead, the hut building association had five under qualified, over worked CFAs on staff.

Upon seeing the situation within the hut association, the tribal leaders turned to the roofers for an explanation. The roofers knew they were in hot water. They also knew they weren't about to take the blame for having abused, oppressed, and generally worked to death all the tribe's framers and replaced them with the CFAs.

True to the nature of all roofers and bureaucrats, they blamed the framing. They told the tribe that they just couldn't find any "real old fashioned" framers anymore. They told the tribe that the framers had "abandoned" their responsibilities by leaving the framing profession when there was no real reason other than lack of commitment to the tribe. They told the tribe that in spite of good treatment, promise of advancement, excellent working conditions, an opportunity to participate in decisions at all levels of hut building, a chance to be a true member of the hut building team, and guaranteed job satisfaction, that you just couldn't find good framers anymore. They told the tribe that CFAs saved the tribe huge amounts of money and did adequate work.

As a result of the absence of qualified framers, huts were not built in time for the rainy season. Many people in the tribe died and there was great sorrow. After two years of living with inadequate shelter, the tribe's numbers decreased. Eventually, the survivors of the tribe were left to live under trees and in caves.

Nurses obviously have a lot in common with the framers in this story. While on one hand we are told we are important members of the health care team, our treatment within this so-called team says otherwise. It's just so much lip service. Nurses are consistently left out of decision making loops. Nurses are not included in board meetings or financial meetings. We are patted on the head and told to be good little team players while, at the same time, we are exploited and manipulated.

Our salaries, benefits, perks, retirement plans, and reimbursement patterns all testify to the fact that we are not equals within the health care "team." Our suggestions, ideas, concerns and solutions are met with resentment by our so called "team members."

Nursing budgets, salaries, positions, promotions and benefits are the first things to be cut when money is allegedly tight. Nurses are the target of every "bottom liner" in the health care system, and are often the chosen "scape goat" for problems within the health care system.

We are first on the team to make sacrifices, and the first to be sacrificed. We are treated unprofessionally, rudely, and with complete disregard by our team members. An example of this is the story told by an experienced nurse who was working as a head nurse on a neurology unit. The chairman of the department announced that the staff was going to be visited by an eminent professor from another institution. The head nurse and other nursing staff were invited to meet this professor when he visited. When the chairman arrived on the unit with the professor, it was obvious the chairman wanted to impress him.

When it came time for the chairman to introduce the professor to the head nurse, he introduced her by saying, "And this is Sally, our head nurse. Sally, this is Dr. X from X University. He is world famous for his brilliant research on cerebral edema." Needless to say, we all know how Sally must have felt at that moment. Then to really get his point across, he turned to Sally and asked her if she could "whistle up" some coffee for the professor and himself while the two of them had a chat in the conference room. "With cream, and two lumps, please, Sally." No doubt, Sally would have liked to provide the two lumps in sugar-free form!

If Sally had truly been a member of this elite health care team, the chairman would never have treated her in such an unprofessional and degrading manner. Even the difference in the way each was introduced to the other sent a not so subtle message of subservience. The nurse was introduced by her first name only, while the physician was automatically referred to as "Doctor." Unfortunately, this happens to nurses all the time. Nurses are given responsibility for the lives of their patients, but we don't merit the simplest courtesy by our heathcare team co-members. This is not team spirit. This is not *esprit de'corps*. This is exploitation and abuse.

Fifty years ago, nurses knew exactly where they stood in

terms of the *health care caste* system and bureaucracy. It wasn't necessarily the place they wanted or hoped to be within the system, but it was out in the open. Though ugly and unjust, it was honest oppression. They were at the bottom of the pyramid and everyone knew it.

Sadly, nurses today are worse off than their forerunners of fifty years ago in respect to their position in the *caste* system. Nurses are the *pariahs.* We are told we are first class citizens of a multi-faceted team, but we are treated like third rate people in every way. The oppression of nurses is built right into the system. It is insidious and more viscous than ever.

Turf wars over patients, reimbursement, status, management positions, funding, education, influence peddling, job positions, benefits, and scope of practice issues are being fought every day within the healthcare system. The battles are fought by gloom and doom merchants who use scare tactics, terrorists techniques, intimidation, and blatant disregard for professional conduct and standards. Nurses are targeted and eliminated.

It is disheartening and extremely frustrating. We may be told we are members of the healthcare team, but the harsh reality is much different. Our survival is at stake, and perhaps our best chance for surviving the turf wars currently being fought within the bureaucracy of the healthcare system is to organize our own "team." What form that team might take is unknown, but certainly the public must be included, and the front line nurses of this country should be the team leaders.

Chapter Twenty

We Naively Believe The Hospital's Priority Is Patient Care, Not Profit

Fifty years ago, the hospital was a place where you went to die. A lot has happened in those fifty years. In addition to the leaps and bounds of medical and technological advancement, hospitals also became "big business." They went from small, self-contained places that offered care and comfort to the sick and dying, to huge, multi-faceted medical complexes. They are owned by corporations top heavy with administrators, whose only job is to lure as many unsuspecting, *heavily insured* patients as possible to their color-coordinated lobbies.

People with degrees in marketing and business administration somehow rose to the top of this heap and began telling people with degrees in nursing and medicine how to care for patients. Money was spent on everything from interior decorators to make the lobbies and patient rooms more alluring, to landscaping companies that added an exterior air of extravagance and abundance which the public couldn't possibly miss.

Hospitals have become laden with administrators who dress in Armani suits, drive expensive cars, and spend their days doling out the money they receive from insurance companies to maintain this delightful lifestyle they've created for themselves. There seems no limit to what hospitals are willing to spend in order to compete for patients. They have a sharp eye for a bargain, and the best bargains they've ever found... are the nursing staffs they employ.

Most hospitals are now creating a deliberate blurring of nursing skills and functions in order to confuse the patients and the public into believing that the role of the nurse is not a specialized one. They have created many new roles with fancy titles like "Registered Care Technician" and "Multi-skilled Worker." These people are usually "cross trained," ancillary personnel who now perform a number of tasks that were formerly only done by nurses. The hope is to convince the public and the patients that just about anyone can do what a nurse does and that it is more cost effective to "downsize" the use of nurses.

In addition to being replaced by under qualified substitutes, nurses are also receiving a bad name in the process, since it is almost impossible for patients, and sometimes even physicians, to determine who is a nurse and who is not. Therefore, it is easy to erroneously presume someone is a nurse when, in fact, the person may be someone whose only formal medical education has been a six week course in everything from sanitizing a room to drawing blood.

Hospital administrators are cashing in on what physicians have known forever, that nurses can be easily intimidated and motivated by guilt, making them easy targets for abuse. They also realize that nurses are idealistic and altruistic and, therefore, willing to work for far less money than they deserve. It is also easy to lie to nurses. Hospital administrations have been doing this for years. They tell them there is not enough money to increase staffing, then ask if they'd like to contribute to the fund for the new building.

This is not to say they don't spend *any* money on the nursing department. Any hospital administrator will tell you that nursing is the biggest "cost center" of the hospital budget. What they often neglect to mention is that, without the nursing department, there would be no hospital and no Armani suits or expensive cars for the hospital administrators. The money they spend on the nursing department is evident when you look at the number of foreign nurses used to staff most hospitals. It costs money to send nurse recruiters to places like the Philippines, Ireland, Puerto Rico, and other countries where women are still willing to be underpaid and under appreciated for their hard-earned expertise. Hospital administrators expect nurses (and women in general) to be grateful for any crumb they throw their way. American women will not tolerate this anymore, so the hospitals do the only smart thing: recruit nurses who are not American. This provides the hospital with a stable of women who are grateful to have jobs and who will tolerate abuse rather than go back to their own countries where conditions are even worse. The saddest part of all is that they undermine the well educated and highly skilled American nurses and deprive American patients of nurses who speak their language and understand and respect their culture first hand.

Yet, both nurses and patients still want to believe that the hospital's priority is patient care, not profit. We may want to believe it, but we'd have a hard time proving it. In addition to subtly trying to replace highly skilled nurses with housekeepers who can draw blood, health care has become increasingly more dominated by huge corporations which purchase hospitals and turn them into profit making enterprises. If you picture the health care structure as a pyramid, there once was a time when the patient sat at the very top of that pyramid, when all efforts were directed at getting that patient better. Today, that pyramid has been turned upside down and the patient sits at the bottom, ready to be crushed by the weight.

Nurses have traditionally been the patients' greatest advocates and we always will be, but we are about to be crushed by that pyramid too. Hospitals have cut wages, reduced benefits, cut hours and increased workloads of nurses while, at the same time, paid themselves hefty salaries, to say nothing of benefits and perks. Hospitals have sucked the insurance industry dry of funds and, as a result, a patient must be desperately ill before an insurance company will agree to reimburse for hospitalization. They will also force the patient to be discharged after only minimal improvement in his/her condition long before that patient is actually ready to go home. This leads to a hospital full of patients who are more acutely ill than ever before and fewer nurses to care for them.

The frightening truth is that we seem to have come full circle. Hospitals are rapidly becoming places where, once again, people go to die. No one knows better than nurses that hospitals think nothing of jeopardizing patient care in order to save money. Nurses are spread thin and are then are expected to rise above all of this and deliver errorless, quality care. What is ignored is the greed and heartlessness of the system. Hospitals have given new meaning to the term "organized crime."

Nurses are more powerless in the health care system today than we were fifty years ago. It is a fact that even Florence Nightingale had more of a say in hospital administration than the nurses of the nineties. Ask any nurse who has been practicing for at least twenty years if she/he thinks things are better or worse today for both nurses and patients. Chances are, you will hear them say things are far worse today than they were twenty years ago. The reason nurses and patients seem to share the same plight is because our roles are so intermingled. When a hospital is "patient oriented," it is also "nurse oriented" and vice versa. The power is always where the money is and we all know where that is: in the thickly carpeted and expensively furnished board rooms.

The advent of the PCA (Patient Controlled Analgesia) pumps is a perfect example of how far from patient centered care we are getting. With this device, the patient is able to administer his/her own dose of pain medication via an intravenous line. Granted, there are some wonderful advantages to this, such as, the patient no longer has to wait for the nurse to draw up the narcotic, sign for it, and administer it. But what we are eliminating here is the nurse's skills of assessing pain, empathizing and comforting. It is almost impossible for a patient to realize he is more *anxious* than uncomfortable, and no machine in the world can replace a kind and encouraging word from an astute nurse who realizes that the best analgesia for this patient is a few moments of her time and attention. But insurance companies don't reimburse for quelling loneliness or calming fears.

It seems we are *replacing* nursing care with technology rather than using them in combination to reap the highest benefit from both. Once again, hospitals are concerned with turning a profit rather than the welfare of the patient. Nurses are being forced to give our ability to heal to machines and money-saving methods that will never live up to the what the patient really needs.

There is an old saying, "You get what you pay for," and it's true. If hospital's *truly* put the welfare of the patients above all else, they would be willing to pay for the highly skilled care of a nurse. When you look at the rate at which nurses are being replaced by people with little or no medical training, it doesn't take a genius to figure out what the priority is.

Cold, hard cash has become what determines the quality of care patients receive today, in spite of all the hard work and good intentions of nurses. The smartest thing we nurses can do is to stop believing our hospital administrators when they try to tell us they can't afford more nursing staff. Instead, let's ask them how many nurses they could hire for the salary of one CEO? Let's point out to the public, to hospital administrators, to ourselves, and to anyone who will listen, that people whose experience is only in business have *no* business restructuring health care. Let's take them to task for dumping the burden of their greed on us and on our patients.

Don't let them laugh at us anymore. Don't let them think for one minute that we believe them when they cry poverty, then spend hundreds of thousands of dollars on consulting firms that tell them how to turn a profit by pulling a fast one on the public!

First and foremost, nurses have always been patient advocates and this is one battle neither we nor our patients can afford to lose!

Chapter Twenty One

We Fight All The Wrong Battles

Any army general will tell you that it's not necessary to win every single battle in order to win the war. In fact, a strategically lost battle can actually throw people off guard, thereby increasing your chances of winning the war.

We in nursing, however, haven't learned this yet. We fight every battle as if it were of major importance. We funnel every ounce of energy into convincing everyone that we are right. Right about whose job it is to file the labs or bring a patient to x-ray. Right about whose turn it is to float. Right about who is supposed to answer patient call lights while we are in report. We give new meaning to the expression "beating a dead horse." We get hold of an issue, any issue, and we don't let it go until the other party admits defeat.

The worst part is that, often while we are busy fighting tooth and nail about something that nobody will even remember in a week or two, we are overlooking crucial issues that will have an enormous impact on us and cause us to lose the war. While we are squandering our time and efforts on whose *turn* it is to float, the bigger issue of why staffing is so poor that anyone should *have* to float remains ignored and unresolved.

We allow ourselves to be faked out, distracted from the real issues. In a sense, a decoy has been set up so that we will focus our attention on the petty issues rather than what is really important. We walk away, smug in the knowledge that we have

just won a battle, while the other side (usually hospital administration) walks away laughing at us. They know how the game is
played and they are experts at it. They know that if they throw us
a crumb we will be so busy gloating over our "victory," that we
won't notice them pulling the rug out from under us on far more
important issues.

For example, the nursing staff in a particular hospital were
up in arms about the "Christmas bonus" they were about to receive. In years past, they had always received an extra $200 or
$300 in their paychecks at Christmas time. This year, however,
they were told that times were hard and they would each be receiving a frozen turkey instead of the money.

Immediately, everyone was ready to fight. They complained
loudly and clearly about this latest insult from administration. They
wrote heart wrenching letters about Christmas presents for children that they could not now afford to buy. Many staff members,
some for the first time, made it their business to attend open meetings with the administration. They argued, they accused and they
hurled insults. One nurse even went so far as to "accidentally"
drop the frozen turkey on her foot as she was picking it up from
the truck, fracturing her fifth metatarsal and smugly announced
that now she not only had a turkey, but also had Christmas day off
... with pay. Finally, the nurses "won." The hospital "gave in"
and announced that everyone would receive their usual $200 or
$300 bonuses.

The nurses were elated. They were self-satisfied and they
felt powerful. They had told the hospital what they could do with

their frozen turkeys and the hospital had conceded. What a victory, or so they thought.

It was shortly after the "Battle of the Turkeys," that hospital administration announced they had no choice but to lay off sixty nurses over the next few months. They were quick to remind the nurses that they were the ones who had insisted on the Christmas bonus, and now there wasn't enough money to maintain their usual staffing levels.

Now everyone knew that a $200 or $300 bonus would not make or break a hospital, especially when there were no visible cutbacks anywhere else, particularly in management. But the nurses were too tired of fighting for every little inch of ground and resigned themselves to the fact that they could never win. Some of them even succumbed to the guilt trip that was being laid on them for insisting on a Christmas bonus. This time everyone was too battle-weary and too frustrated to attend administrative meetings or to write heart wrenching letters. This time, sixty nurses lost their jobs.

It was a brilliant tactic on the part of the administration, who knew right from the start how the nurses would react to the insult of the frozen turkeys. They knew how short sighted and easily discouraged nurses can be and they used it against them.

The issue of a $200 or $300 bonus is not a small one but, in this case, the nurses had been set up to divert their attention to a smaller insult, while administration was plotting an even bigger one. What nurses sometimes don't realize is that choosing our battles carefully is half the strategy of winning. Who really cares whose *turn* it is to float or to rotate to nights? The louder we argue about such pettiness, the easier it is to lose our credibility, to say nothing of our stamina. Once a person starts complaining and making a big issue out of petty annoyances, that person is quickly labeled a "chronic complainer," no matter how legitimate the complaints, and people turn a deaf ear to them.

Nurses also seem to have a hard time being direct. Perhaps that is because our jobs and sometimes our very survival in the profession depends on our ability to be tactful. Unfortunately, our tact sometimes works against us. How many times have you seen the following scenario played out?

Several staff members are annoyed with one of their colleagues for any number of reasons: she's always late, she argues about her assignment, she doesn't get her patients' meds out on time, whatever. After a number of nurses complain to the unit manager, a staff meeting is set up for the sole purpose of confronting the person and trying to resolve the difficulty.

As everyone gathers in the conference room, the unit manager asks who would like to start the meeting. Immediately, all eyes are downcast and no one volunteers. The unit manager then decides to break the ice by stating that there have been a number of complaints about people being late, argumentative, and inefficient with the meds. Still no one says anything, so she continues until it becomes clear to whom these complaints are directed.

Sometimes there is one brave soul who confronts the person and ask her directly why she doesn't get her meds out on time and if there is anything the others can do to help her get more organized. This may cause the person to get defensive and start blaming the problem on the inefficiency of the pharmacy, even though everyone else seems to get their meds out on time.

It is at this point where that tactful "nurse" behavior kicks in and everyone starts complaining about the pharmacy instead of the original subject. Granted, the subject may be uncomfortable, since there is usually no easy way to confront a co-worker, but once again, nurses will choose the wrong battle to fight and then wonder why nothing ever gets resolved.

For a group of people who have such outstanding communication skills when it comes to our patients and their loved ones, we seem terribly ineffective at communicating with one another. We seem to have a very hard time staying on track and deciding what our most important issues are. Perhaps this is because we have so *many* seemingly overwhelming problems in our profession that it's difficult to determine their degree of complexity and importance.

Our greatest advantage is that, as nurses, we know the importance of triage. We know how important it is to refrain from scattering ourselves in a thousand different directions, and we know that sometimes you have to put aside the minor problems and funnel all of your energy into the more serious and life-threatening ones.

Chapter Twenty Two

We Waste Opportunities

At times it seems that we just don't have enough energy to get through our forty hours-plus work week and all the other chores and responsibilities we have due to our families or other obligations. Sometimes the "mountain" just seems too high to climb, and we can't bear to look beyond the next eight hours of work. We are so overwhelmed we simply won't allow ourselves to consider the possibility of adding one more thing to our schedule. We feel we can't take on or manage one more task.

There are other times when we aren't necessarily overwhelmed, but we find ourselves plowing a deep rut of routine, boredom, and sameness that seems to go on and on. We keep our eyes down and our backs bent simply because it has become a way of life. We fail to see what might be out there for us because we never look up. We simply keep plowing the same old fields without realizing that nothing seems to be growing in the ruts. Our curiosity becomes so dampened that it simply doesn't exist anymore. We become intellectually under stimulated, and our thinking becomes stagnant.

Both conditions, being over extended, over worked and existing in an endless rut of sameness, can cause us to miss opportunities that offer us new skills, new ways of thinking about things, or a chance to use our minds and our curiosity. There are opportunities for learning, sharing, and experiencing ways to do things that might be more interesting or more efficient. The fact is, there are opportunities out there that we could avail ourselves of that would enrich us as individuals and as professionals.

But, as a twist on an old cliché says, "You can lead a person to a well of opportunity, but you can't make them dip the cup and drink." So, it is with nurses sometimes. There are lots of reasons for people turning down opportunities. The pop psychology books can tell you all about them: fear of success, fear of changing, fear of alienating ourselves from others because we learned something new, guilt over taking time to do something just for ourselves, or career burn-out. The list could go on and on.

Everyone who has ever turned down an opportunity can give you a rationalization for why they opted not to go for it. Talk to any nurse and you will hear an excuse why he or she let an opportunity sail by that could have brought something positive into their lives. We don't have to let this happen. The point is, what has happened to our joy in learning and exploring just for the sheer pleasure of it?

Nurses are some of the most curious human beings on earth with keen and active minds. We have a natural interest in how things work, in what makes things work, and more importantly, how things can be made to work better. We are curious about people's stories, their lives and experiences. We enjoy *knowing* and using what we know. Sometimes, however, we seem to forget this and waste our opportunities to do what comes most natural for nurses: learn and grow.

Identifying and meeting opportunities head on takes a change in attitude and an awareness of what goes on around us and in the world. To identify opportunities, we must redirect some of our energy. We must free our minds to develop a focal point that takes us beyond our everyday lives and our own preoccupations.

Some of the best opportunities are right under our noses, in the institutions where we work, among the fellow nurses with whom we work, with other health professionals we come in contact with, and within our communities. Many places of employment offer courses, lunch time talks, and presentations on clinical topics, tuition reimbursement, grand rounds, hospital sponsored courses and seminars, open library systems, computer courses, or health and fitness programs for employees. These are just a few opportunities we could take advantage of simply by making a phone call and signing up.

Employment Assistance Programs offer counseling and other support services that could help us with personal or career issues. After all, if we don't have our own lives in order, how can we help patients with theirs? Take advantage of weight management classes, join a smoking cessation program, or enroll in a stress management program. Many institutions offer these services at a reasonable fee to employees.

Hospital employee clubs often negotiate with local businesses and universities for discounts on tuition or membership fees. Why not take advantage of them? The whole point in grabbing an opportunity when it comes around is the benefit we derive from the experience as a person and a professional. Opportunities add richness to our lives. Opportunities stretch us as nurses and as human beings. Opportunities allow us to use our creative talents and introduce us to new interests, new people, and new experiences.

Why not organize a journal club among the nurses in your hospital? Why not get a BRN provider number and earn continuing education units by attending the journal club or other conferences formally organized by your co-workers? Why not get together and share educational videos or audio taped lectures? Why not join a local book club just for the fun of reading good books and sharing what you liked about the book with others?

Sometimes we need to broaden our horizons beyond nursing to include business courses, personal finance seminars, self improvement seminars, or other educational and informational type courses or experiences. Take computer courses, telecommunication courses, writing courses, and public speaking courses. Join community business clubs. Participating in these kind of opportunities will lead to other opportunities we never even dreamed of.

Nurses are natural entrepreneurs. Many nurses start up their own businesses. They identify a need, scope out the market, and provide the service or develop the product. A Los Angeles nurse saw a need for affordable, well supplied earthquake kits. She networked with the medical supply company representatives that she knew through the hospital where she worked and negotiated a discount for medical supplies. She got her business license, and was able to buy other supplies wholesale as well.

She started assembling the kits in her guest bedroom. She

marketed them to friends, co-workers, neighbors, church members, and other contacts just before Christmas as affordable, useful, and unusual Christmas gifts. Her orders increased, and she moved to her garage. She hired a high school student to help her assemble the kits. With the supplies, she included straight forward first aid instructions and public information materials on emergency preparedness that were available free of charge to the public. Eventually, her business grew, and she now has office space and three employees.

An east coast nurse decided to become a health care consultant. Her first step was to write letters to several corporations marketing her services. She offered to train the company employees in CPR on site. Being a CCRN and qualified CPR instructor, her qualifications were already in place. Her contract expanded to the point where she needed to buy her own resuscitation doll. She went to her bank and, with some creative negotiation skills, she was able to secure a small business loan. This was to be the first in several business successes for this talented, ambitious nurse. The success stories are all around us; we simply have to be open to the opportunities that come our way in the form of ideas and chances to use our natural talents and creativity as nurses.

Another opportunity that we nurses often let slip between our fingers is the multitude of chances we have for networking. Other professionals know the intrinsic value of networking within their immediate cadre of co-workers, their institution, their industry, and community. Networking should always be a two way street. The power of networking is exponential when it is recip-rocated. Ask any successful person what they think about net-working. They will be able to tell you a dozen stories off the top of their head about how networking resulted in a concrete benefit or opportunity. In fact, without networking this book would not have been written.

Nurses must look for opportunities to be visible. Visible to the administration (so we can express our views every chance we get), visible to the public (so they stay informed about the profes-sion and what we have to offer), and last but not least, nurses must never miss an opportunity to be visible to the press or the media. These are all golden opportunities to represent ourselves and our profession. We should never miss a chance to talk about ourselves and our work. We should each be our own best spokes-person and press agent.

Creating opportunities and taking advantage of them when they come our way requires an open mind, curiosity, energy, a sense of adventure, and the willingness to do something just for ourselves. There's something out there for every one of us. Al-ways remember, when one of us takes advantage of an opportu-nity, we all gain. When one nurse is successful in a unique or special way, we all benefit. We just have to suspend negativity, adopt an " I will do this for me" attitude, look to the future, and hang on for all we're worth.

Chapter Twenty Three

We Believe A Nurse Is A Nurse Is A Nurse
(A Rose By Any Other Name)

Have you noticed the latest trend in hospital name tags lately? They display catchy little slogans like "Partners in Practice" or "Comrades in Care," followed by first names only. There is no "RN," "LPN," or "Nurse's Aid" to identify exactly whom is caring for the patient. Much like the perky little waitress you find in a franchised restaurant, nurses are fast becoming nameless, faceless, interchangeable, anonymous widgets in the soon to be franchised healthcare business.

It is frightening to realize that our very identity, the thing we have worked so hard for, is quickly and subtly being stolen right out from under our noses. This blending of nurses with people who are far less educated is being called "partners in practice," or any other cutesy little catch-phrase the hospital can dream up. Call them what you like, but don't forget to call them "replacements," for that is truly what they are. It is much cheaper for the male-dominated, bureaucratic hospitals to employ these people rather than pay for highly skilled, professional nurses. It is a way of making us dispensable, portable, disposable, replaceable "members of the health care team," and it is an incredible insult to our profession. The fact that we accept it is a travesty.

The hospital, however, had ways of telling us we were interchangeable long before "first name only" name tags became accepted. "Floating" us from one area of expertise to another is just one of the many ways hospital administrators like to reinforce the message that nurses are nothing special. To their way of thinking, any nurse should be able to handle any type of patient.

It doesn't seem to matter that the physicians who treat these patients do several *years* of specialized training before daring to prescribe or perform any type of procedure on them. Can you imagine coming to work one day to find that the hospital's only neurosurgeon is home with a bad case of the flu, and that the orthopedic surgeons will be doing all the brain surgery today? After you pick yourself up off the floor from laughing, you have to wonder why that is so much more far-fetched than floating a neurology nurse to the orthopedic unit. Apparently, the people who sit behind desks, making these decisions for nurses, still believe that nurses only perform menial tasks and therefore do not require any specialized training. That is precisely why people who are not involved with direct patient care have no business making decisions for those of us who are.

Case in point: Three hours into her shift, an experienced orthopedic nurse was told she was being "floated" to a general surgical unit. The nurse protested, explaining to her supervisor that she was in the midst of transfusing one of her post operative patients and needed to finish pre-operative teaching with a patient scheduled for total hip replacement in the morning. In addition, she had just finished assessing her eight other patients and still had to document it. The supervisor told the nurse that she had "tunnel vision" because she only saw what was going on in one small corner of the hospital, and therefore failed to see the "whole picture." Naturally, the supervisor's opinion was the superior one (according to the supervisor), and if the nurse refused to go, she would be written up for insubordination.

The nurse decided that she would "obey now and fight later," since she really didn't have time to argue. Besides, she knew from experience that it was a losing battle. She gave report to the already overburdened nurse who would take over for her, then found her way to the unfamiliar surgical unit.

The first patient she went in to assess had undergone a hemorrhoidectomy that morning. The patient asked the nurse to help him to the bathroom. The nurse assumed that it was all right to ambulate the patient and assisted him to the bathroom, where he promptly turned a ghastly shade of white, rolled his eyes back, and crumpled to the floor. When help arrived, the patient was revived and transferred back to bed and the nurse was told that most people with hemorrhoidectomies faint the first time they get up. She was instructed further that it is always a good idea to have two people assist the first time a patient like this ambulates.

The nurse then went into her second patient's room. This patient had had a rhinoplasty earlier that day and the nurse found her standing in front of the mirror, studying the rather large amount of blood that had drained onto the nasal tip dressing. The patient looked upset and asked, "Nurse, should I be bleeding this much?"

The nurse reassured the patient that some bleeding was expected, and helped her back to bed. Since she didn't have any recent experience with this type of patient, the nurse decided to page the on call resident, just to be on the safe side. When he called back and she described the situation to him, the resident was very annoyed and reprimanded the nurse for interrupting his dinner for such a "routine" problem. He then curtly asked to speak to "someone who knows what they're doing."

The rest of her shift didn't get any better. She spent twenty precious minutes searching for the Percocet, which she later found out was kept in a locked drawer in the top of the med cart since it was used so frequently on this particular unit. A patient's daughter asked her for a progress report on her mother, and the nurse sheepishly had to admit that she'd never cared for this patient before. She would have to find someone else who knew the patient to get back to her with the information. Another patient called his doctor at home to complain that he had waited twenty minutes for his nurse to bring him a urinal and didn't anyone know what they were doing around here?

When at long last the shift was over, the nurse remembered that she still had to document the blood transfusion on her patient on the orthopedic floor. Upon entering the elevator, she encountered the nursing supervisor with her coat on, leaving for the evening. The supervisor smiled at the nurse and said, "See? It wasn't so bad, now was it?"

The nurse went home (eventually), feeling defeated, exhausted, and inadequate. She decided she was too tired to fight anymore and took comfort in knowing that it would not be her "turn" to float again for at least another week or two. Not unlike the slave masters of the eighteen hundreds, the health care system has this nurse (and many others like her), exactly where they want her, too tired and too busy to revolt.

How sad that we readily accept defeat like this! How tragic that we are directed by people (nursing supervisors to senior management), who have no idea how specialized nurses have become and how valuable it is to have them in their areas of expertise. How did we let this happen? Can you imagine what would happen if we documented the inefficiencies, errors, and patient complaints that result from this type of practice and sent copies to Risk Management, the Board of Trustees, and the CEO? And if "floating" is absolutely necessary on occasion, why don't we demand extra pay or *some* kind of compensation for all that added stress? Why shouldn't we invite the CEO of our hospitals to lunch and educate him/her on the dangers of the practice of "floating?" And, while we're at it, educate him/her on the absurdity of lumping all nurses into one category.

Speaking of absurdities, a critical care nurse, who was also a tenured professor at the local university, had just received her PhD in nursing. When she was paged over the intercom as "Dr. So-and-So," she was told in no uncertain terms that she was *not* to be referred to as "Doctor" while in the hospital, because it was "too confusing." Can you imagine telling any of the PhD's in psychology that they cannot be referred to as "Doctor" while in the hospital because it's too confusing? Are we being told that a PhD in nursing is less valuable than a PhD in anything else? Can you think of anyone besides nurses who would tolerate this type of insult?

Our skills, knowledge, and experience are not utilized or

recognized to enhance the overall quality of care. Once again, we are being told that no matter what our educational level or professional accomplishments, a nurse is a nurse is a nurse. Worse yet, some of us actually believe it.

Nurses have an obligation to speak out for the benefit of our patients and our profession. And yes, there will always be some casualties before significant change is made. Many of us have been or will be punished and labeled for pointing out the inadequacies of the system, but our silence will do far more damage. It will only benefit those who would keep us "in our place." That is not the place we anticipated when we entered the nursing profession to utilize our knowledge, skills, and intuition to care for the sick.

With health care in this country being completely reorganized, nurses can no longer afford to allow themselves to be beaten, driven, managed, coerced, and intimidated by anyone, particularly people and organizations who know *nothing* about caring for the sick. We are simply going to have to find the courage and the strength to do what we know must be done. We have our work cut out for us.

Someone once said that there is no such thing as a well adjusted slave. In all probability, that person was a nurse.

Chapter Twenty Four

We Define Ourselves By Our Weaknesses Instead Of Our Accomplishments

To err is human, but to accomplish is divine.

Mistake-aholic: *A person suffering from a disease manifested by a continuos fixation and discussion of their own mistakes and the mistakes of anyone else who is willing to talk and listen.*

- Teresa Allen, RN

Nurses generally tend to be accomplished individuals with a variety of interests, hobbies, skills, and talents that are successfully applied to their nursing careers, as well as their personal lives. We are artists, writers, crafts people, singers, dancers, poets, athletes, volunteers, actors, martial artists, business people, students, and a million other things, in addition to being nurses. As nurses and individuals, we excel in many areas. However, in spite of all our talent, experience, and accomplishments, it is still difficult for us to measure our personal and professional worth by the positives. All too often we define ourselves by our shortcomings or mistakes. We tend to dwell on the mistakes and ignore our accomplishments.

To illustrate this point, think about this. When was the last time you had a chat with a co-worker or other nurse and heard them say something good about their work? When was the last time you heard another nurse tell you about her accomplishments?

Such as when she relieved a post-op patient's pain with a creative combination of pain medication and relaxation techniques. Or the time she helped a newly delivered mother learn how to breast feed her new baby who was born with a lip deformity. Or the time she saved a patient from receiving the wrong medication because the pharmacy sent up penicillamine instead of penicillin. Did your co-worker tell you about the article she had published in a magazine, or the seminars she teaches, or the research project she did that resulted in a change in nursing practice? Did you bother to genuinely listen if she did try to tell you about these things?

Think about your conversations with fellow nurses. Do we ever tell each other about our successes, our accomplishments, our achievements, or our professional goals? Rarely do we feel comfortable telling others about our accomplishments. Even more disturbing is the fact that we often negate the accomplishments of our fellow nurses by not showing genuine interest and enthusiasm for their accomplishments and efforts. We turn a blind eye, not only to our own accomplishments, but also to the achievements of our fellow nurses.

It's as if we simply can't bear to say or hear anything good about ourselves or our fellow nurses. Instead, we define ourselves by our mistakes. If you put five nurses in a room together for any amount of time you can bet that eventually all five of those nurses will deliver up a "confession." Each nurse, in turn, will tell the others about her worst mistakes or failures. This behavior does not serve us well as professionals or as individuals worthy of praise and recognition.

We have all done this at one time or another. There will be horror stories about medication errors, patient accidents, failure to prevent a complication, IV's that ran dry, and any number of other errors or mistakes. Each nurse will tell her story bravely in a contrite voice while the others listen earnestly, barely able to wait for it to be her "turn" to talk about her biggest mistake. We simply love hitting ourselves over the head. One would think that we get enough of that without doing it to ourselves and to each other. To put this problem into perspective, can you imagine a group of physicians, hospital administrators, lawyers, or politicians sitting around telling each other about their mistakes? Can you imagine hearing physicians eagerly, openly, and explicitly discussing the times they almost killed a patient? Can you imagine a group of hospital administrators in a room talking about the millions of dollars they squandered and wasted because of their bad decisions? Can you see a group of attorneys looking each other in the eye and giving a blow by blow account of how they lost their client's case because they didn't do their research or because they didn't know the law? You're lucky if you can even imagine these scenarios because, you can bet your stethoscope, it doesn't happen. Ever.

So, why do we do it? Why is it that nurses are so eager to air their mistakes instead of their hard earned accomplishments? Why aren't nurses able to accept their mistakes, learn from them, and then move on? Instead, we react with extremes. When we find ourselves "right" about something inconsequential, we gloat.

When we make a mistake, like any other human being, we agonize forever and forever, it seems. Why must we wear our mistakes like a badge of honor? *What are we, mistake-aholics?*

To err is human, but to accomplish is divine. This should be our personal credo. We should celebrate our accomplishments. We should take the time to tell others about our achievements, our professional goals, and our ideas. We should return the courtesy of those who listen to our stories by showing genuine interest and pleasure when they tell us about their successes. Nurses have plenty of accomplishments. Our successes far out number our mistakes. It is in our best interest to remember that and behave accordingly.

Chapter 25

We Believe We Have No Power

Your whole body, from wingtip to wingtip, is nothing more than your thought itself, in a form you can see.

Jonathan Livingston
Richard Bach

We left the discussion of power for the last chapter in this book. It seemed obvious to us that we would not be able to fully realize our power as nurses without first taking care of the business in the twenty-four preceding chapters.

When nurses talk about possessing power, they often think of power that is external to themselves as individuals or as nurses. We think about power in terms of the amount of control we have in determining our immediate work load, our working conditions, and financial compensation. For nurses, power translates directly into control. Consequently, when we feel we have no control, we also feel powerless. This view of power, however, is limited in both the associated rewards and responsibilities.

Power is more complicated. True power goes beyond being able to control, manipulate, or enforce. True power *enables.* A truly powerful person possesses the potential to change, to transform herself or himself, or to redefine her sense of self within reality. True power transcends control issues. This is how nurses should view power.

We should strive for the power to redefine our image and

our sense of self as nurses within the reality called the health care system. So, where does this power come from?

In that classic story, *The Wizard of OZ,* everything the main characters so desperately wanted, came from within themselves. The lion who wanted courage, the scarecrow who wanted a brain and the tin man who wanted a heart, eventually learned that they had never found these things because they had been looking for *someone else* to provide them. The so-called wizard's job was easy. All he had to do was point it out to them. When each of them finally stopped doing the meaningless "busy work" of traveling the yellow brick road, they looked inside themselves and found the answers. Answers that had been there all along.

And so it is with nursing. We have been far too busy following our own yellow brick road, paved with paperwork, nursing diagnoses, and TQM meetings, to realize where the *real* power lies. When we take the time to look within ourselves to discover that power, immense change occurs.

It is no accident that nursing has such a high turn over rate. We are always searching for that perfect job or perfect situation in a frustrated attempt to find a way to practice nursing that doesn't deplete our very *souls*.

But as Dorothy in *The Wizard of Oz* discovered, if you can't find what you're looking for in your own backyard, it probably doesn't exist. *Real* change only comes from within. If she had figured that out in the first place, she wouldn't have had to battle with the wicked witch or fly through the air in a spinning house. If nurses would realize the individual power that resides deep within us all, a lot of wicked old witches would be eliminated from our lives.

Imagine this book to be a health food smorgasbord. Each dish or idea should be sampled. Fill your plate with the dishes or ideas *you* most need to replenish your hope, strength, and courage. For without these, change cannot occur.

Simply stated, we are what we believe. However, certain behaviors, attitudes and actions contribute to what we believe about ourselves. This is why awareness of these things is so important. Without awareness, the change process can't begin. The goal of this book is to bring about awareness of certain things we do as nurses that can cause us to self distruct. Our destruction must be prevented at all costs. We are far too valuable to let this happen. For when nurses self destruct, everyone suffers, even those who don't value our contributions.

In a world where money, position, and possessions are always the bottom line, nursing is an exotic bloom in a desert of lost values. We are the only thing blooming in this wasteland of greed. Though they may not realize it, the world cannot afford to lose us.

Teresa Allen, RN
Joan Brady, RN
Laura Gasparis Vonfrolio, RN